THE Autobiography
of Jesus of Nazareth and the Missing Years

Richard G. Patton

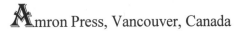mron Press, Vancouver, Canada

THE Autobiography

* * * * * * ✡ * * * * * *

THE Autobiography
of Jesus of Nazareth and the Missing Years

By Richard G. Patton

Published by: **A**mron Press
Suite 157
2496 East Hastings Street
Vancouver
British Columbia
Canada
V5K 1Z1
Tel : - (604) 253 3283

ISBN 0-9682437-0-3

9 780968 243701

Cover artwork by Gordon S. Schuck of Vancouver Island, Canada. Tel : 604 - 757 8354

Printed in Canada

PREFACE

In 1993 I moved from England to Canada. Through a remarkable series of 'coincidences' I met and came to know Laurel Phellan, who later went on to write *'Guinevere- Truth of a Legend'* - the channeled memories of her life as the almost-mythic English Queen of Camelot. This was my first introduction to 'Channeling' - a term I had never even come across before.

My limited understanding of Channeling is that 'Beings' of Light who have never existed in physical incarnation, enter the willing body of a Channeler (similar to trance mediumship) and communicate to us through their Channel. It is claimed that these "Beings' are of a Higher Spiritual frequency than ourselves and have a greater understanding of Soul's purpose and its relationship with the Originating Source.

For a period of ten years prior to meeting Laurel Phelan, I had been working on a screenplay about the 'Lost Years' of Jesus. In passing interest I inquired of another leading Channeler (Elizabeth Adams) if I had been in physical incarnation anywhere near to this time in history. The Channeled reply was that, not only was I incarnated but that I had been with Jesus for many years - even being present at 'the Last Supper'. This response was so astounding that I reasoned that it must have been conditioned by my not-inconsiderable Ego. I then approached another renown Channeler, and without going in to specifics, was given the same response.

Terence Hayes, an independent film producer, unbeknown to me, had a Channeling in which he questioned the veracity of what I had been told. Everything was confirmed and even more than I could have suspected.

Being a pragmatist, I then determined that I would undergo Past-life Regression Therapy and see if it was possible to access these traumatic times. The first results were interesting, but I still couldn't determine if it was my Ego responding or a genuine Past-life memory. Further Regression Therapy confirmed my experiences - beyond death.

The following is my heartfelt attempt at fleshing out the wonderful human being I knew, and we have historically come to know, as Jesus of Nazareth. Initially I had intended that it be my observation of this Great Being of Light, but as the writing progressed, I found it had become the autobiography that now follows.

AUTHOR'S FOREWORD

I don't ask that anyone believe what I have written, I simply ask that each person weigh it in their hearts. If anything resounds with you, then it may be truth. If it does not resonate - then please return the book for a full refund as outlined at the back of this book.

There was a time when a true man of God walked among us and his influence has been conscious for almost two thousand years. The time has turned and another Great Master is now influencing this planet and its volatile consciousness. Details are unnecessary. All that is required is that we recognize that we cannot go forward without opening our hearts to each other. It is time to love our enemies - for we are them.

With Joy and Light
Richard G. Patton

NB. The author may be contacted by Email at : -
104742.1432@Compuserve.com

ACKNOWLEDGMENTS

Drunvalo Melchizedek and his work with the establishment of the Christ grid which now overlays the planet. Also for his reintroduction of the Merkaba breath and the knowledge of counter-rotating fields of energy.   Sri Harold Klemp, the Living Master of Eckankar who taught me the structure of Belief.   Krishnamurti who first directed my attention to the wealth of information that lived on in India with regards to Jesus' travels.   Dr. Maxwell Cade who taught me all he could about Biofeedback and Altered States of Consciousness.   Sifu Chan Yik Yan who taught me the Taoist arts of healing and Luk Hop Bat Fa.   Sathya Sai Baba for his unspoken guidance.   Master Hilarion and it's continued purpose.   The Divine in everything, which I have so resolutely ignored until this time.   To Spencer James who opened my heart.

And in conclusion - my adored wife Norma, without whose Love and devotion, this book could never have been written.

* * * * * * ✡ * * * * * *

P erhaps now should be a time for profound thoughts and timeless words - yet somehow I find it hard to focus. Could I really have been so wrong? Even those who have been close to me these past few years, those I thought understood... Even they! Perhaps I expected too much of them? Perhaps they demand more of me?

Even though the oil lamp burns above, this night is darker than any I've known, darker still than the tomb I knew beneath the Sphinx. Somehow, then it was a matter of willing consciousness, where now, it's unwilling flesh. In a curious way, the pain of the soldier's lashes comfort me. With my back mostly dry now, areas of blood still moisten when I move. The pain helps to fix me in this time and place - not the ethereal quality of fasting. I want no escape as though between worlds - I want to know for certain, that as flesh I claimed the Christ consciousness and as flesh I failed. Till this moment I believed flesh could live in Spirit, now I know - consciousness is everything. There are times in my life that I achieved a clarity unclouded by thought, but now, I sit in this dank dungeon where hundreds have passed before me. Like them, I'll soon be forgotten. Perhaps we are the sum of our thoughts? If this is true then I must be pain personified, because I find it hard to reach beyond this pain to happier times.

Through all my years of training, I denied my youth. Living in the moment, I forgot the happy years of playing with my brothers and sisters. Perhaps that was the nagging shadow that pricked my heart whenever I saw children play - I hadn't give them the love they deserved. Where I was trained to live in the moment, children lived it naturally. In a deeper part of me, I knew they were closer to truth. Where better to hide the most beautiful gem, but in direct view? Our adult minds are too clever to just *be*. The mind needs explanations, theories - so that we can claim them for our own. It cannot comprehend anything outside of itself. How the universe must laugh, to see such arrogance! We even attempt to section time, by using the candle. This night is the same as any other, yet to me, it's far longer than any I've known.   A child would know that, but not chose to have it any other.   For me, I wish the daylight had come.   My heart beats, feeling as though it resonates against the damp walls, rebounding against the sharp cuts of the High Priest's lash.

My thoughts turn to Nazareth.   As I regularly climbed that dusty hill, date palms gave way to the heavy fragrance of firs and cedars.   My ears would always pop as I neared the crest.   How I loved the late afternoon breeze as it came up from the valley below. The crows hung suspended in the breeze along the escarpment and children tried to hit them with stones.   The crows were always smarter and I don't ever remember any of us hitting one.   Almost a thousand feet below, the peasants worked in the patchwork fields, moving like ants at our feet.   How pitiful they were.   Although I didn't know it then, inwardly I sensed the injustice.   One third of their produce went to the landowner; one third to the taxes and the remaining third helped them eke out a living - a living that rarely stretched beyond a single basic meal a day.   Joseph said it hadn't always been that way, but I found it hard to believe.   We often played along the banks of the little stream, racing our sticks down the narrow course.   By mid-summer the water no longer showed at the surface and we had to help with carrying water from the well.   In a way, it was a blessing that the stream was so restrictive, since it meant that our village remained small and friendly.   Less than two hours walk away was the wonder-filled city of Sepphoris.   Here there was an Acropolis, a bank, heated baths, law courts and even a Gymnasium.   I loved to visit the Greco-Roman city but was more than glad to return home.

There were many happy times.   The first I can recall was when the Tibetan Hor first visited my family in Nazareth.   I was little more than two years old at the time.   He arrived with others but it was as if they weren't there.   Although we had never met, my heart burst with an uncontrollable love when I first saw him.   He paid me little notice, so I continued playing in the sandy courtyard. He went to my youngest brother who was still in swaddling clothes and sleeping in the trough for the animal feed.   Father had a fever and my mother was concerned that we might catch it, so we had been sleeping outside on beds of hay.   Even at that age, I always preferred sleeping under the stars anyway. Hor and the others made a fuss over Joses, but soon appeared disappointed. They had presented various objects to him and he had shown little interest in them. It seemed curious to me that they should expect anything of a child less than a year old. The night had been very hot and he was still tired. The Tibetans had traveled far and I could see were very disappointed. I continued playing on the dry ground. Using a twig, I scratched figures on the ground. One of the other Tibetans drew Hor's attention to me and my scratchings.

"The sign of Pisces," Hor exclaimed in amazement. I hadn't really noticed, but there on the ground, I had drawn three small fish.

"What's his name?" they asked.

"Yeshu. Yeshua ben Joseph," my mother had proudly said.

The three men looked at each other as if in unspoken agreement. Lun, the younger of the Tibetans, then laid out some items on a silk headscarf: various incense and items of gold. I could feel the need these men had that I should take an interest in their offerings. Somehow they paled into insignificance as I felt drawn to old Lun. Hidden in the deep folds of his large Tibetan sleeves, I found a smooth pebble. Scratched into the surface were three fishes. I threw his stone on the ground beside my scratchings.

"The Dalai Llama has been reborn into the land of Judaea. Our journey is ended," Lun spoke as all three men prostrated themselves at my feet. For the first time I felt discomfort.

How strange that these memories should come to me now, but then again, maybe not. That simple action as a child had set the course for my life. I hadn't known it then and even now, I can only glimpse the vague pattern of light. As fine as any spider's web, I sense that even the smallest action in my life has resonated towards this very center and the web is soon to be complete. Does the spider understand the strange concentric beauty it weaves, or is it driven unconsciously towards that center where it rests in total harmony with the vibration of the universe.

Like the gentlest breeze, I feel the dawning light, yet not with physical eyes. It's as though my heart has become my center. I see, feel, need - with my heart.

The Tibetans spoke of Herod and terrible times. As a child, I hadn't fully understood, but soon we were hurriedly escaping in the night - across the desert. There were many sandstorms and we protected ourselves by lying on the ground, close against the stomachs of our animals. Father's fever grew worse. One night I watched as a pale blue light, which I had begun to notice around several people close to me, grew dimmer around my father. His eyes were closed, but a gentle smile came to his lips. Suddenly he opened his eyes, fully alert and turned directly towards me.

"God be with you Yeshu," he whispered and closed his eyes. Despite being held in my mother's arms, warm against the bitter cold of the desert night, I felt terribly alone. Although he was my mother's husband, I somehow knew Joseph wasn't my father by blood. It was many years before I did learn who my biological father was. For days he remained unconscious as we traveled South. Finally we arrived at the Temple of Zoan, where the Priests applied various foul-smelling poultices around Joseph's neck. That was the first time I had seen crystals actively used in healing. After a month there was no sign of the illness that, under normal circumstances, would have ended in his death. Soon Joseph returned to his usual good humor, though he was never again as strong.

For several years we remained guests of the High Priest and Priestess of Zoan. They were very kind and took special care of my mother. For the first time, I saw my mother as a human being, separate from myself. It was unsettling and reassuring at the same time. I had always seen her as an extension of myself - constantly tending to my every need, but there in Zoan, I saw her in a new light. It didn't become obvious until my cousin John joined us with his family. Although close to my mother, Elihu and Ruth addressed her as 'Holy mother and Protector of Light.' For days at a time, my mother would disappear and then return without explanation. She seemed to grow distant from me. It wasn't that she cared any less, it was just that there was a strange light in her eye that before had only encompassed me. Now it seemed to touch every living thing without discrimination. Also, when we had first arrived, the priests of the temple were always talking to her about Spiritual matters I had little understanding of. Joseph sat back and enjoyed the prominence my

4

mother had assumed. In this light I became closer to Joseph. By his simple actions I understood more about humility than I later learned in years from 'learned men' and their lofty speeches. In the later years, whenever my mother spoke, everyone listened. Sometimes, I even saw the chattering birds hold their peace. Those were the happiest years of my life.

John was my best friend. There never seemed to be enough hours in the day for us. We would often take a donkey out into the desert to explore for scorpions and snakes. I thought he was too serious though. He was always telling me off for playing jokes on the priests.

One time, I caught a Blind Snake - the ones that burrow beneath the desert sands for bugs and larvae. Knowing they were harmless to man, I slipped it into one of the priests cassocks while he ate. We always ate our meals in total silence. Suddenly the priest let out a scream as he felt the snake move under his clothing - and fell off the bench to the ground. John, who was always more athletic than me, quickly thrust his hand up the priest's clothing and pulled out the snake. There was complete silence in the hall. The High Priest, Elihu, looked long and hard at John before speaking in a low voice. Although the others in the hall continued eating, placing their attention on the food in front of them, none could have missed his words.

"John" he spoke, choosing his words to carry the most resonance. "Only a fool, or the perpetrator would act in the way you just did." He paused for the words to register on John's young mind. "A fool wouldn't know if the snake was deadly or, as in this case, harmless." John's eyes were cast down in shame. "The perpetrator on the other hand would have no fear in acting the way you just did, since he would know. Continue with your meal." The High Priest turned directly to his food without judgment. John sat back down, his face redder than the ripest pomegranate.

My heart pounded so loudly I feared my words wouldn't be heard.

"Please may I speak Older Brother," I blurted out.

"When we eat, we ONLY eat, Yeshua!" His words were kind but firm.

"But I've something important to say," I pleaded.

He considered for what seemed an age, but was probably only moments.

"Then we will listen," he finally spoke. As one, the Brethren placed their food bowls on the table and without turning in my direction, placed their total attention on my words.

Never have I felt so humiliated or degraded. "Older Brothers, it was me that placed the Blind Snake in Brother Theudas' cloak."

I had expected that to be all that need be said, but the silence hung in the room and no food bowls were picked up. I realized the inadequacy of my words.

"I thought it would be funny to get a reaction - from what is, a harmless creature. Unintentionally, I would have demeaned Brother Theudas for my own selfish pleasure. I apologize deeply and thank my Cousin John for displaying his true act of courage. Also, I ask that I may be allowed to wash the bowls of all the assembled brethren for the next month - so that I may be given the time to fully understand this lesson in ego."

"Your wish is granted Yeshua ben Joseph." That was all he said. There were no recriminations, no looks of condescension. The brothers smiled kindly on me. I don't think it was deliberate, but the weight of the shame hung more heavily on my young shoulders *because* of their kindness. The wooden eating bowls of the brothers have probably never been cleaner, or more cared for as they were that month. Only John and I spoke about the incident. He had shown such courage, not knowing whether the snake could have been deadly. Still, his love for his brother had been greater than his fear of a painful death. How many times that memory has carried me through dark times.

"We create our own lessons, we are our own teachers," the High Priest had said. "Anyone who tells you otherwise, does not work with the Light." As a child I thought that gave me license to evade the fruits of my actions. 'It was an accident; That was lucky; I'm not responsible....' - phrases I had used, and believed!

Looking back, I see now how each footprint in the sand was unique and guided. Some actions seemed incidental, but I see that even the smallest gesture had its consequence. There's an emptiness in the pit of my stomach, that I should have wasted so much time in not being Conscious - not being in the moment. Now I'll be put to the ultimate test of my faith. How gossamer thin that link between Faith and Belief? Which persuades me now - my heart or my head? In my head I know that death is a transition of consciousness, but with the promise of Crucifixion ahead, my heart pounds uncontrollably. Will there be a quick pain as those iron spikes are driven through my wrists? That would be bearable. If it's a lingering pain that pervades my sinews, will I be able to overcome the call of the physical? Each heartbeat draws me closer to the dawn and the beat of guards' sandals on cobbled stones.

I seemed to be stronger in my youth - certainly braver. How did I ever find the courage at twelve years of age, to openly question the leader of the Sanhedrin? The words tumbled from my lips as though already crafted in stone. They had no answer to my question of temple sacrifice. They, who had the power to order any man's death by stoning, had no answer to a child's simple question. It was as if a storm had risen from deep inside me. How could they possibly believe that the Father Spirit would in any way be served by the blood of some innocent creature. Their coffers would twice be served: once by the purchase of the Temple coin and secondly by the purchase of the animal in the Temple courts. Now as I sit at the end of my days, I see how clearly that twelve year old boy had foreshadowed my confrontation with Caiaphas all these years later. Yet, that was when I first met the Prince. By 'met' I don't mean knowingly. He had watched me in the Temple, on the periphery of the crowd. Word had soon spread that one, not yet become a man, dared to question the Temple Leader. A chill runs through me now, just to consider the audacity of my actions - no one questioned the Men in Black. The Prince had listened with care and seemed to have an insight I was never granted. Some are able to see such things. For me it was never so easy - I trusted and felt. When a man spoke, his words either rang true, or not. How easy it would have been to be able to see into a man's soul and know his true intention - but that wasn't the way for me. In my heart, if his words sat comfortably, I trusted he spoke truth. If he lied, his energy seemed displaced - his words seemed to echo as though first in his head and shortly after from his mouth.

My father had been very angry that I stayed behind in the Temple. Traveling back after the festival, the caravan of people had been too large for him to immediately notice. He thought I had been caught up in conversation with one of the other travelers also heading back towards Nazareth. I thought it had just been his anger at my not remaining close to the main group. Only years later did I learn, it had been because of his fear of the Sanhedrin and the repercussions my actions might have. The Sanhedrin governed every aspect of local life, no matter how remote. Wherever there was a Temple, the eyes and ears of the Sanhedrin were also present.

The Sanhedrin controlled all temple sacrifices. It had even become illegal to sacrifice outside the walls of Jerusalem. By this act alone, the leaders of the Temple had assumed almost unassailable power, since every true Jew was expected to make token sacrifice to Yahweh. Generations before, the edict that every able-bodied Jew had to attend the Temple in Jerusalem at least three times every year had been passed. Attendance was expected for the three sacred festivals of Pesach, Sukkot and Shavuot. As if this were not difficult enough for the poor, the Sanhedrin even prescribed what level of sacrifice was to be made. Much social credit was gained by families able to sacrifice a calf. For the poor, two small pigeons was the minimum expected. In order to be certain the sacrifices were 'clean', the Temple controlled the sale of sacrificial animals and their coffers grew correspondingly. The poor, more than anyone else, hated the Men in Black. Beside the social stigma of being penniless, they were now subjected to the open disdain of the Temple Keepers.

The Prince learned where I lived and followed us to our home in Nazareth. He offered to take me with him to India, claiming that he felt he had been 'called' to bring me before the Spiritual Masters. We had more food than we needed and more rooms than people to live in them, so Mother declined his generous offer. She explained that our community of Essenes provided for our own and we didn't need any further assistance - no matter how well intended. I was told - not for the first time - that my ancestry dated back to King

David and that I had social duties to fulfill. She explained all this to the Prince - yet he still managed to persuade her.

Seeing those around me, I had always understood my good fortune of being born into an affluent family. As was the custom, I learned a craft at my father's side. He was a builder and traveled every day to Sepphoris. His mastery was in the construction of grand doorways and arches of stone. Over the years I had learned how to carve in both wood and stone. By getting me to carve elaborate designs into his structures, my father could demand higher wages for the work. My mother often told him to wear a cloth over his mouth when working, because of the Stone Sickness. Joseph always agreed with my mother, but never wore any protective cloth. He had learned the trade at his father's side and *he* had never worn any cloth. Most of the Greek stone-workers wore a thin leather face-guard, which they regularly soaked in water; but for the Judaean workers, this was considered Hellenistic vanity and they preferred to work in the traditional manner. Few of the Greeks ever caught the Stone Sickness, though most had the incessant cough. It seemed that only the Judaean workers coughed up the dark blood. Whenever I saw Joseph coughing up blood, I could see in his face that he had known my mother had been right. He had good days and he bad days. Increasingly as I grew older, his day were bad. Although he loved his work, he knew it was a cruel mistress. Joseph taught me his love for working with the hands. Had the materials we were working on been animate, I suspect Joseph would have been a great healer. As it was, the unforgiving cold of the stone, sucked the heat from his blood. In fact, at the time of the Prince's visit, Joseph had suffered particularly badly from the sickness and lay in bed with a fever. In my later years this trade allowed me to travel without need of assistance from my family. Often while he worked, I would go off and explore the new city. The Gymnasium was the most interesting. There the people studied Philosophy, Latin and Greek, gymnastics - and wrestling! Athletics was not something we as Jews excelled at. Perhaps it was our inbuilt modesty. Very few Jews were prepared to display our naked bodies in front of strangers. Of course, in every generation the younger members want to rebel against their elders. We were no different and it was from these ranks that the

Gymnasium drew its members. At first I was shocked to see the naked wrestling and the runners, but after some time it became almost unnatural to see athletics any other way. We had long been exposed to the magnificent Greek and Roman statues, but here in the gymnasium we could actually see the bodies on which they were modeled. Some adopted this new found 'Greekness' to extreme, by having an Epispasm. To the utter horror of the elders, they had the foreskin stretched back over their penis' - effectively undoing their circumcision. Whenever the elders protested at this rejection of their divine heritage, the young men claimed they were being 'civilized'. One young Greek pointed out that had God required us to be circumcised in order to bear witness to his truth, we would have all been born circumcised from our mother's womb. The Greeks were masters of debate and the elders counter-argument was more bluster than substance.

As if this infringement on our culture was not enough for our elders, the daily wine and olive oil on the table, was being replaced my Greek produce imported from Rhodes. The elders paid lip-service by objecting, but invariably chose the Greek product over our own more coarse produce.

The Prince was very persuasive. Of course we knew about India, but not the Eastern state of Orissa. He said that he believed I was to play an important role in coming changes - though he never specified what 'changes' he was referring to. Although I didn't understand, his words stirred a distant memory - or was it premonition? This Indian Prince of Orissa wanted me to travel back to his homeland, so that I could be taught by the great spiritual men of the East. I was excited at the prospect, but said nothing. My uncle, Joseph the Arimathean, argued against it. Being the oldest of the children, I knew my place was at home, supporting the family. All my study with the Rabbis and in the Essene community, counseled that I remain in Judaea. Strangely I suddenly found an older head on my shoulders and demanded my birthright, which was to travel the Silk route with this gentle Prince that I barely knew. My eyes locked with my Uncle's. In that moment, I knew he had other than 'brotherly' feelings towards my mother - and he knew I knew.   My mother, appeared oblivious of this sudden antagonism. My Uncle's objections to my traveling, vanished like a mist at dawn.

I had no comprehension of just how beautiful the desert could be.   I had often seen the caravans arrive in the marketplace with their riders covered from head to foot in white or black robes.   Sitting high up, apart from the hands holding the camel guide ropes, the only visible part of their bodies was the narrow slit across the eyes - but what eyes!   Their eyes gleamed from the desert sun as though they were privy to secrets of the universe that us mere mortals could only guess at.   Unconsciously I had yearned to travel with them.   Now I was and I knew it was pre-destined.   As the last rays of the sun descended behind the vast dunes, the sands took on the color of blood.   At their crests, the palest golden flames appeared to grow as the sand was whipped into the air.   Sometimes small funneling winds would dance across the sides of the dunes.

'Sand Devils' one of the drivers called them.   To me they were Angels, in fact my first glimpse of what the Rabbis called, 'Jehovah'. In the golden light, the dancing funnels of light revealed the - coherence of chaos!   Each grain of sand moved in perfect accord with the wind eddies.   There was no resistance, only perfect harmony.   Suddenly I understood how limited Man was.   He looked to intelligence that he could identify with, an intelligence he could understand.   How naive! Here was an intelligence, guided by some Universal energy which man so easily dismissed as 'Nature'.   Here was God in all it's finery and we chose to dismiss it, because it didn't fit our expectations.   It was as if a curtain had been drawn from my eyes. I had been taught to expect choirs of Angels and beings of light descending from fiery skies.   How betrayed I felt by those 'learned' men.   All the time, the reality of God and Universal Love had been less than a heartbeat away!   The desert had a living silence that even now feeds my soul at its memory.   There were no distractions, no teachings that could hold me separate from the burning love that transcended even death.

It was almost one month before I learned why the Berbers watched me with distrust.   At first I put it down to their natural reluctance in talking with strangers, but it was Mahmud, one of the Berber children who told me.

"It's because of your camel," he said as we drew a skinfull of water from the oasis. He wasn't going to say any more, but I needed to know. I gave him a fresh orange to ease his reluctance.

"It's the camel," he said again.

"But there's nothing wrong with the camel. It never gives me any trouble."

"Exactly."

"So why should I be disliked because of that?" I pleaded.

Mahmud looked around, to be certain he wasn't overheard.

"That one is dangerous - always biting the other camels and sometimes, people too."

"He's changed?"

Mahmud looked me in the eyes and simply nodded.

"And they blame me for this?" I asked, confused.

"A camel's character is cast in stone - yet this one is changed." He walked away with his skin of water and the juice of the orange running down his cheek.

I was shocked. These people who I had shared bread with, laughed with and bathed with - thought I was touched by the devil!

In the evening I sat close to the Prince so that we could speak in private.

"Why should they distrust me, when I haven't done anything," I spoke downward to the ground. Without taking his gaze from the campfire, the Prince seemed to be looking for the answer in the embers.

"There comes a time, when mind is confronted with something outside of itself. It will kick, bite and curse, so that that thing be denied. If mind accepts something outside of itself, it is no longer King," he spoke quietly so others shouldn't hear.

"Fear?"

"Where fear exists, there can be no love. Without love there is only darkness. Nothing is more disturbing to darkness than light." He had nothing further to say on the subject and we both sat with our thoughts. Finally I could stand it no longer.

"But where's the justice? It was the camel that changed, not me. Why should I be silently accused, when I've done nothing?" It seemed so unfair that I should be judged guilty without any appeal.

"Justice is a fine word, but it can only be applied to the works of man," he spoke as though hearing the words in his head from some third party.

"Are you saying God isn't Just?" I asked, astounded at the suggestion.

"I only say what I've heard from wise men in Persia and India," he tried to console my confusion.

"And they say 'God isn't Just'!?"

"They say 'God is'. Any other description or adjective applied is simply Man separating himself from God, through the mind. God has no need of praise - God is."

"But what about the camel? I did nothing?"

"Far to the East of India, there was a wise man by the name of Chuang Tsu - perhaps five hundred years ago. He said that merely by a butterfly flexing its wings, chain reactions can occur that will even create violent storms. When you spoke in the Temple, I saw a young butterfly flex its wings." He looked directly at me.

"Your words confuse me sweet Prince. One day I may be educated, like you. Then perhaps, the truth of what you say may be revealed to me. I don't understand what you say, but in my heart I feel you are speaking truth."

"Until that day, only I and the camel will know the truth," he smiled. Then his mood turned serious. "Yeshua, do you trust me?"

The words caught me by surprise, as though I was being tested.

"Of course!" I immediately answered.

"Yeshua, I ask again - do you trust me?" he insisted. Suddenly I realized what he was saying. I had answered as I had been taught, so as not to give offense - even though it was true. He watched me closely.

"You answered me as though we were separate," he spoke as if I had insulted him.

"Prince, I trust you with my eternal soul and you were right, I spoke without seeing us as one Spirit. Please forgive my lack of understanding. Why do you ask such an obvious question?"

"To focus you in this moment, in this time. You were still with that camel," he smiled that infectious smile I loved so much. It was like a child's smile. A smile that tries to stifle an outright laugh, but the eyes tell the full story.

"You may not understand now, but one day soon, you will. You have concealed within you, a bright light. It's as bright as the largest star in the night sky."

I had no idea what he was talking about, but I trusted him with my life.

"I'll take you to men who will teach you the mysteries of God's universe and that small light, will be turned into a blazing inferno. Because I willingly take on this responsibility, I ask one favor in return?"

The clandestine way he spoke and the heartfelt plea excited and, at the same time, filled me with dread. What could I possibly give, in return for the offer of fulfilling my deepest desires?

"I ask that, when you're asked to speak Truth, answer people's words, not what's in their hearts. Truth is a dangerous animal, Yeshua. You're young yet and won't understand. Many people call on truth but few really want to hear its voice?"

"It seems so little to ask, and so strange," I answered, again aware I had answered from the wrong center. The Prince, was also aware I had answered from my head and not my heart.

"For you, what I ask is an enormous undertaking. You just haven't had the opportunity to realize it yet, but you will. What's your answer?" He asked in a way that suggested my whole future might depend on it. Now as I sit on the eve of Crucifixion, I realize he asked too much!

"I swear by my faith, I will always speak to what is being asked, not what is behind people's words and in their hearts." We both rested our right hands on the others left shoulder and the deal was sealed.

"You're a spark that'll be nurtured to flame. The danger is, that you're surrounded on all sides by parched grassland. That privilege carries with it enormous responsibility. You must watch which way you turn or the whole world will be set aflame," he spoke in all seriousness. Without a further word, he pulled the hood up over his head and lay down to sleep.

"One more thing, Yeshua," he spoke, his head turned to the darkness.

"Yes?"

"Mask your light." He turned his head to see that I understood. I simply nodded.

"Good," he turned away again and, from his deep breathing I could tell, was soon asleep. I slept little that night - or any night since. Although I hadn't fully understood his words, they seemed to carry a continued resonance that acted on a deeper level. Whenever I rested, my body generated extraordinary heat, as if my atoms were being refined by some ethereal flame. It was neither comfortable nor uncomfortable, it was simply a state of being. Over the years it's become less noticeable. It isn't that it's gone away. I feel that after all these years of training, my physical being has been raised to the same frequency as the inner fire. There is no more resistance. I am!

That same night as I lay awake beneath the stars, I experienced a rare event of consciousness. Lost in thoughts of inner fire and destiny, I felt something move beneath my tunic. There was a hesitant deliberation and I knew it was a snake. In the desert there are few snakes that don't have a lethal bite. How I wished that this might be Brother Theudas's returned joke, but I knew it wasn't. I had two choices: I could try and make a sudden move and try to grasp the snake by the head, avoiding its fangs or two; lay still as death and hope the creature find its way back out into the darkness. Surprisingly, it felt warm against the smoothness of my belly. The memory of the incident with the Blind Snake and my cousin John, lay etched as clear as daylight in my mind. The snake, unable to find an exit around my armpit, slithered its way up to the opening around my neck. Without any conscious control on my part, I let out a deep moan as though that might ward off the snake. It didn't. The snake raised its head above my chin, its unblinking gaze meeting mine. In that moment I had an unshakable knowledge I had a debt to be paid from a previous life. The nature of the debt was unclear and unimportant. All I knew, with timeless certainty, was that at some deep core of my being, I had agreed to pay this debt before entering this incarnation.

When the strike came, it was lightening fast and struck just below my left ear. Reflexively, I sat bolt upright as the Prince's scimitar cut through the night sky, cutting the reptile in half beside me. Holding my neck as firmly as strength would allow, I watched transfixed as both halves of the snake continued to writhe in the sand.

Immediately the night was filled with the shouts of the wakened caravan and many people offering advice. The Prince took control, ordering a flaming brand to be brought from the campfire. The last thing I recall was the faces of the camel drovers suddenly turning away as the brand was pressed hard against my neck.

Several days later I began gradually drifting back to consciousness for a few moments at a time. I was conscious enough to see the Prince had been waiting on me and had applied some form of poultice to my neck. A sheepskin had been tied around both my legs, to which the Prince was constantly applying cool water.

As my strength began to return, the Prince would only allow me to drink a hot liquid that had been made from the most pungent herbs and it took all my willpower not to be sick as I swallowed.

"The snake would at least allow me a quick death" I joked as I finished the cup.

The Prince smiled. "If you had been well, that brew would *literally* have killed you. It is only ever administered if death is otherwise unavoidable."

"At what point do I cross the line of being well - just so that I know when this stuff reverts to being lethal again?" I asked, concerned.

"I don't know. This is the first time I've used it," he smiled.

"Suddenly I feel much better - enough not to continue taking this!" To this day I still don't know if he was joking.

"You entered the Yogic state several times," he spoke seriously.

"Yogic state?" I queried, the term unfamiliar to me.

"Your heart stopped beating for several hours. Our Yogis in India are able to do it at will. The valves to the heart remain open so that blood can pass but there's no discernible heartbeat."

"Then, I died?"

"Your men of medicine would have declared you dead. The heart maintains a mild pulsing, which allows the blood to keep circulating. That's how men are able to be buried alive - some for months, or longer," he answered, seeing he had caught my interest.

"But I don't know how to do that," I answered, confused. "It must take years of training?"

"I have no answer, Yeshua. But it does, as you say, take many years - perhaps lifetimes?"

"But I have no memory of such lives, so how could I use such a technique?"

"I don't know," he answered genuinely perplexed. For some reason I felt unable to speak about the three Tibetans who had greeted me in my youth - even to the Prince. When I say 'youth' and here I was, still only thirteen years old, it was as if, through this illness, I was no longer a boy. I seemed no longer the carefree youth, but instead, the man in training. There seemed to be a very direct course my life would now follow. Inwardly I felt tears at the loss of my youth, outwardly I appeared equally as mystified as the Prince.

"Will you forgive my request?" he suddenly asked.

"Request?" I queried.

"To address what is in men's words, instead of what is in their hearts," he answered.

"I forgive you anything sweet Prince. Now, I even owe you my life," I tried to placate his concern.

"I had no right to ask."

"What is there to 'forgive'?" I queried, not understanding his concern.

"If I hadn't spoken, the snake wouldn't have bitten you," he solemnly spoke.

"How can you possibly believe *you're* responsible?!"

"It's a hard thing to explain. When we get to Benares, there will be men wiser than me to explain." He paused, seeing his answer wouldn't satisfy my question. "Around us there are potentials - possibilities. These possibilities may not become manifest in this lower world, unless the energy of thought is applied to them. - You see?" he asked to see if I comprehended what he was trying to convey. I nodded so that he should continue.

"I asked that you block or restrict the natural energy that would be expressed through your voice. My directing both our consciousness' towards this limitation, manifested the situation. For myself, I know this is beyond me. My mistake was making you focus *your* attention in such a restricting manner. It's like a broad river being forced through a narrow pipe, the force of the water may well split the carrier. While you've been sick I've understood just how important it is that you begin your training as soon as possible." As he spoke, his eyes misted with tears. I couldn't tell if the tears were for happiness or sorrow. The seriousness of his words denied any further questioning. How I wish I had asked him at that time, how he had come to know these things. But then again, no. The time wasn't right and I wouldn't have understood anything that came close to the truth of such things. I was still thirteen and more than enough revelations lay ahead.

"I forgive you," I spoke uncomprehendingly. He reached forward and kissed the back of my hand after the manner of the priesthood. Around the campfire, several of the camel drivers saw the Prince's gesture. Moving closer to speak among themselves, it was apparent they considered me a bad omen.

The following weeks seemed to blend into one extended moment. It was as though the experience with the snake was a small rock penetrating the surface of my consciousness, yet below, a vast mountain was beginning to make itself known. To those around, I appeared distant, perhaps aloof. I no longer had the communication skills to placate their concerns. It was as if some unseen Master Chef had retrieved all my essential inner elements and was preparing to reconstitute a far finer meal out of the same elements. My vision was clouded by a pale mist of light that allowed nothing to retain it's hard outer structure. Instead, I saw intention before there was action. I saw a fine golden light in the heart of those around me - even those that now viewed me as a craftsman of the black arts. Most of all, I saw the love. The finest web touched all things, as if it was all one inter-connected organism within the limitless body of God. From time to time, try as I might, I was unable to stop myself from outright laughter at this unusual realization. My heart simply filled with a boundless love and yet, I found myself restricted within this meager body and its meaningless concerns. It had seemed hysterically funny and there was no way I could communicate, other than through laughter. How they must have wondered at this strange youth.

The Prince attempted to speak with the camel drovers, attempting to explain that I wasn't possessed - but my whole body was sensitive to their distrust.

After the dryness of the Sind desert, it was a great relief to finally reach India. We parted from the main caravan in the Market place at Kairpur. Never had I seen such spices or color! The finest embroidered clothes were exchanged for sweet smelling woods and handfuls of the deepest blue Lapis Lazuli, stood on wooden stalks, ready polished. This was a feast for the eyes after the bareness of the past few months travel.

With the return to civilization, my sensory revelations gradually faded. I was no longer able to directly see the thoughts of men or the universal web of love. Often I questioned whether they had in fact happened, or if it had just been a trick of the desert. When I was able, I voiced my experiences and concerns to the Prince.

"When we return to Jagannath I'll take you to see Udraka, he'll know," he said, grateful to be allowed access to my thoughts. He had often mentioned Udraka, his mentor. "'If anything turns your mind to God', he would say, 'then it is true'." The Prince's voice always softened when he spoke about Udraka. I looked forward to meeting him.

"I have some business to attend to five days ride to the North of here. So I'd like to leave you with some friends," the Prince suddenly announced. I asked to be allowed to go with him, but the Prince was adamant. "There are dangers it wouldn't be wise to expose you to - and I have promised your Uncle." It had been a long time since I'd thought about my Uncle Joseph. He had never actually shown undue affection to my mother, yet I felt it was only my presence that kept him from doing so. I felt uncomfortable just thinking about him.

"Joseph presumes too much on my behalf."

"Nevertheless, I gave my word." The Prince wouldn't be dissuaded.

The Prince's 'five days ride to the north' took him away for ten months. When he returned, he apologized for the delay - but spoke little about what had kept him. He had left me in a community of Jains just outside Pallipana. The Jains lived communally and grew all their own produce. Their foods were simple, but wonderfully prepared. Their spices and flavors come to my mouth just at the thought of them, especially the curried 'Ladies Fingers' or Bindi Baji. A far cry from this dank prison.

The Jains were the gentlest people I had ever come across. Their belief system was based on total non-violence, to the extent of gently sweeping the floor in front of their feet so that they shouldn't inadvertently step on any insects! They taught me much about the Vedas - the ancient Hindu texts, said to be ten thousand years old.

"If God wills it that an insect meet it's fate under your feet, why should you deny God's will?" I asked innocently. I immediately sensed that I had given offense.

"By killing the insect, we take on it's Karma - and we will have to return for another life to pay for it," the Guru answered. "This way, we walk as a life-giving God and take on no debt." I hadn't pursued the point.

I pretended to understand and nodded my gratitude in thanks for being corrected and illumined. As much as I loved their gentle ways, there seemed to be a fatal flaw in their outlooks. Their actions appeared guided more by the fear of not doing the 'right' action, that by the love of God - even if that meant you were to be the instrument *through* which someone should receive a painful lesson. This was the first integrated teaching I had come across since leaving the bosom of my Judaic faith. Their teachings of complete love and peace towards all living things, deeply impressed me, despite areas I viewed as being naive. Their commitment towards sweeping even the smallest insects from beneath their feet, wasn't directed by false humility as I had seen in so many of my own Synagogues; it was directed from a genuine sense of universal love. It was fascinating to experience a total belief in a single God, that paralleled my own, yet was so different. Nevertheless, I was very glad to see the Prince return. How often during those months I had reminded my self of my promise to the Prince and how hard it had been to keep - even though he had released me from the obligation. Looking back on it now, something like anger grew in me at the time. Perhaps it was just frustration, that the Jains had spent so much time devoted to their spiritual outlook, but it was all passive. Being so young, I felt that God would want us to be active - be a co-worker with it. It was the way I was to lead my life and even now, I'm not so sure I wasn't right!

"In a few weeks we'll reach Jagannath. There I'll introduce you to Udraka. He lives very simply, but is recognized throughout all India as the greatest of all Hindu healers. His knowledge of the elements - water, fire, earth, wind and air - is second to none." I could see in his eyes how excited he was to be seeing his old mentor again. How strange that, when we are happy, no matter what age, the child shows through our eyes?

The next day I had the extraordinary experience of seeing my first group of Sadhus. A group of grey and mostly naked figures made their way towards us. Our party, though larger than theirs, left the path so that these strange men shouldn't have to deviate from their course. Even a woman among them stood completely naked, her hair unkempt and hanging disheveled down to her knees.

"They have renounced all life," the Prince explained. "The grey ash they cover their bodies with, is the ashes of the dead that have been cremated along the great riverbanks."

They passed us by, some unseeing, others talking animatedly to elemental forces they appeared to see around them. My heart grew heavy as I saw not the slightest glimmer of joy in their faces.

"Many have Siddhi powers - they can hypnotize with a look. It's better not to have dealings with these people." I wanted to stop and speak with them. I wanted to know what pain could drive them to renounce the wonder of nature, the sweet smell of the ground after the rains, the beauty of the Moonflower... I respected the Prince's reticence and held myself back. Suddenly, one of the Sadhus stopped and angrily turned towards us. He took a three-pronged ceremonial staff and pointed it towards me. One of the Prince's men moved to strike the man for what he said and the Prince intervened.

"What did he say?" I asked.

"It's nothing," he answered unconvincingly.

"I want to know," I pressed.

"He says that creatures of the night don't ask for a flaming torch to light their way. Why do you, Yeshua ben Joseph - he knew your name - why have you come to destroy them?"

"How does he know my name? Why would I destroy anyone or anything? Ask him," I demanded, again feeling unjustly attacked. The Prince rode his horse between me and the Sadhus.

"They're crazy people - leave them! Perhaps he heard your name from people who traveled before us," the Prince spoke, unconvinced himself, but wanting the Sadhus to pass unhindered. It was the first time I had seen the Prince exhibit anything like fear, so I relented and allowed them to continue without my answer. Why would a Prince fear a handful of insane men who appeared to wash in the ashes of the dead?

The Palace at Jagannath was the most splendid set of buildings I had ever seen. Peacocks strolled unconcerned through the colored marble halls and inlaid jewels sparkled from the walls. Everywhere colorful and uniformed servants attended to the most minor of needs. There were even men whose only purpose was to hold fans of ostrich feathers over bowls of fruit, so that no insects could settle. Others stood at the entrance of the large open galleries so that any passer-by should only feel a cool breeze on his neck, instead of the intense Indian sun. We had been greeted royally by the Prince's cousin and a fabulous meal that defies my limited vocabulary was presented before us.

After we had eaten I asked that I be excused, so that I might go for a walk and enjoy the night breeze. The Prince and his cousin had much to talk about, so my presence wasn't missed. The sound of the Cicadas filled the air and large flying insects flew frantically around the open braziers. Although oil lamps lit the grounds, many concealed in the boughs of the largest banyan trees I had ever seen, the full moon provided more than enough light. There was such order in the Palace grounds that only the sudden shriek of the peacocks, reminded me of the limitations of this privileged world.

Hundreds of ornate fountains played into long pools of dark sparkling water. How far this was from my beloved desert. Curiously I felt stifled and had to leave the restriction of the lavish grounds. Turbaned guards sat or strolled beneath the arched entrances, brewing small cups of bitter tea. Recognizing me as a visitor, they attempted to dissuade me from leaving the grounds. Through sign language I firmly explained that I needed to leave 'civilization' for a little while. In order to make my point, I confidently strode past and out into the night. After several moments of hurried and concerned debate, I found myself being followed by two of the guards, walking ten paces behind. I glanced back and their scimitars gleamed keenly against their sides.

We had hardly gone fifty paces, when out of the shadow of some clustered huts, a group of disheveled people came, moaning and holding out their hands. They ranged from stooped elderly men hardly able to walk, to young children with gleaming eyes and eager fingers. The guards ran forward shouting to intercept them, their scimitars raised with both hands above their heads. The sorry grouping momentarily shrank back. One woman complained bitterly, indicating her hunger and her right to ask this stranger for food. The most able man pressed forward, remonstrating with the guards. Then, as if to make some gesture towards my face, he stretched out his arm. His hand was parted from his wrist faster than I could see the guard lower his scimitar. I didn't know how to react. I stood there in shocked disbelief as the ragged figures hurriedly backed towards their meager huts in silence. The man sank to his knees in silent shock, blood spurting from the stump of his arm, before falling unconscious at my feet. Before the realization could register with me, several hands lifted me from the ground and forcibly returned me to the Palace grounds and the Prince.

The Prince's cousin seemed angry with me, which made the whole situation even more surreal.

"What were you doing, leaving the grounds, Yeshua?" the Prince asked, questioning my sanity.

"I said, I wanted to walk - alone," I answered, confused that I should be the one being questioned.

"You said 'walk', but not outside the grounds," he returned in disbelief.

The Prince's cousin exchanged several angry words with him. Not wanting to give a direct translation, the Prince spoke cautiously, trying not to give offense.

"The guards told you not to leave?"

"They tried to dissuade me, but I don't speak Hindi."

"Then that'll be my first duty, to teach you," he spoke solemnly, as though he had been in some part to blame for this whole horrendous situation.

"But I don't understand? That man could be dead because of the guard's action," I pleaded.

The Prince's cousin called to his principal body-guard and instructed him on some matter. The Prince stopped speaking so that he could listen. On a gesture from his cousin, the Prince explained in full.

"India is a country of great extremes - the unbelievably wealthy and the unbelievably poor. Everything remains in order because we have the caste system. Each man knows his place. Without this hierarchy there would be unimaginable bloodshed and chaos," he qualified. "Those people are less than the lowest of the low. They have afflictions and disease."

"But they meant no harm," I argued.

"That man was known to the guard. He had wet leprosy. He has been known to threaten travelers with the disease, unless they give him food." The Prince was interrupted by his cousin who wanted to be sure that I understood the whole picture. "There are countless numbers like him in India and if it became known that my cousin supported them, his Palace would be surrounded by plague and disease."

"Then perhaps he should share his wealth?" I asked, attempting not to give offense. The cousin inquired as to what I had said. The Prince waived it off as if it was of no consequence. The cousin looked closely at me, suspecting that the Prince hadn't been altogether truthful.

"Would one drop of rain in the ocean make it taste any less of salt?" he asked, pointing out the hopelessness of my suggestion. I still didn't have any idea of just how vast India was, or the extent of the divided caste system.

"Because a man is blind, should I not tell him he's walking towards a cliff!" I answered, surprised at the Prince's equanimity under the circumstance.

"At a more 'appropriate' time we'll discuss the caste system," he stifled the discomfort he felt so that his cousin shouldn't detect the animosity in my argument. He smiled towards his cousin, reassuring him that all was well.

"By creating the situation..."

"I didn't 'create' the situation," I quickly corrected. The Prince's cousin leaned forward, concerned at my tone of voice. The Prince continued as if he hadn't been interrupted.

"By creating the situation, and the guard acting with kindness..."

"Kindness," I again interrupted, unable to contain my agitation.

"Yes, kindness. He had every right - in Hindu law - to remove the man's head from his shoulders. Instead, he removed the 'offending' hand - from which he will recover. By your actions tonight, you have improved that man's life beyond his wildest dreams," he spoke waiting for my expected question.

"I'm at a loss" I gestured helplessly. The Prince smiled at my confusion

"One of Gohar's personal physician's has been dispatched to the man's hut - and for the rest of his natural days, neither he or his immediate family will want for anything," he spoke nodding so that his cousin should know he had reached the salient point. I smiled my nodded understanding towards Gohar. He smiled back, pleased that I should know of his great generosity. Inwardly I was furious that *anyone* could believe that such injustice could be rectified for a sum that the Prince would, in all likelihood, never notice from his coffers.

The next day we left the Palace. Perhaps it was coincidence, perhaps it was the Prince's awareness of my discomfort - I suspect the latter. I felt so torn, seeing the countless numbers of poor and yet living the life of unimagined wealth and comfort myself.   Out of consideration for the Prince, I held my tongue.

"Thank you for not speaking what was in your heart , Yeshua," the Prince spoke as we traveled along the red dust road.   "Especially since I released you from that bond". I looked towards him and hoped he didn't recognize my disappointment with his endorsement of Gohar's attitudes.

"Perhaps it's wrong of me to impose my expectations on another culture," I tried to excuse.   Inwardly I knew that there was no justification for treating *any* human being in the way that leper had been treated.

"Today we see Udraka," he spoke, hardly containing his glee.

Just before dusk, we arrived in a small mud-baked village, from which aromatic scents rose from hearth fires.   The smells triggered off remembrance of happy times, which, try as hard as I might, I couldn't call to mind.

Towards the end of the village, with dogs running in and out of open drainage, a rotund figure of about forty years beckoned us forward in welcome.

"Udraka," the Prince spoke, his voice almost trembling with emotion.   As we came closer to the light I could see he had tears in his eyes.

"Welcome Sanjitji - and the young Rabbi," he came forward, stopping the Prince from prostrating himself before him.   I was shocked that the Prince should feel so much for a teacher, that he would happily demean himself - and in such basic surroundings.

"Babaji, this is Yeshua ben Joseph.   I saw him speaking in the Great Temple of Solomon.   Although many spoke, I only heard one voice in my heart - and knew it was my duty to bring him to your door," the Prince formally bowed both to myself and to Udraka.

"Come Yeshua, the Prince gives me too much honor.   Really he speaks of my tea - which *is* famous throughout India," Udraka made light of his fame and beckoned us forward.

"You called me young Rabbi - and you knew we were coming?" I queried, perhaps rudely.

The Prince and Udraka exchanged knowing glances. It was obvious that there was much I was to know and yet, had been told nothing.

"Your clothes," he explained, but I still wore the robes of the Bedouin - nothing that would suggest doctrine. "And word of travelers carries faster than any Arab horse. But come, let's take tea."

He lead us into his hut. At first I thought the ceiling was much lower than I had anticipated from outside. As my eyes became accustomed to the flickering light of the fire, I could see that bundles of dried herbs and grasses hung thick from the rough beams. The fire was fueled by the dried-dung of water buffalo which, beside creating a sweet woody smell, kept off the mosquitoes that hung in clouds everywhere else. Sitting cross-legged around the fire, Udraka poured out the creamy brown tea that had been cooking above the flames. The tea had been cooked in the milk with what I later learned was nutmeg, grated into it. I've tasted it many times since, but I'll always remember that first time at Udraka's. Perhaps he *was* famous throughout India for his tea? Unlikely as it seemed, my satiated thirst could have persuaded me otherwise.

That night we spoke for many hours of things pertaining to the world. Udraka had a surprising and intimate knowledge of Judaic law, yet had never traveled to Judaea.

"I hear many things from travelers," he explained. Yet, how many Rabbis - because it would have taken someone with extensive knowledge of the Law - could have traveled to this insignificant and remote village, enough that he should be so well informed? Before I drifted into sleep that night, I felt I had come home. By home, I don't mean a finite place but a state of serenity and wholeness. It was instinctively recognized, rather than consciously remembered.

"The founder of your nation was a Hindu," he said one day without prompting. Udraka was so playful, I was never sure when he was joking or when he was serious.

"I'm serious," he encouraged, seeing my look of doubt.

"But it was Abraham," I argued, sure of my ground.

"The name is a corruption," he simply stated.

All the Rabbis I had studied with had all had unshakable faith that the founder of Judaism was Abraham. To state that he was anything other than a Jew, within the Temple precincts, would be to condemn yourself to death.

"Why do you say something so outrageous?" I asked, slightly offended. Although I was a Nazarene Essene, the central precepts of Judaism were inviolate - or so I thought.

"He was a Brahmin and lived in Chaldea. He was a pious man devoted to the God Brahm. Sickened by the carnal ways of the priests, he kept himself away from the temples. When a famine swept his land, he traveled to Zoan in Egypt - the land of the Initiates." As he mentioned Zoan, happy memories of diving head-first off steep dune crests with John, and rolling forward on the soft sands below, came to mind. "After many years study in the Temple there, he traveled back to the plains of Canaan and Mamre, where he lived and taught. This is where the name A-Brahm comes from." He continued nonchalantly collecting the berries from various bushes while I remained rooted and thunderstruck where I stood. It was as if a shaft of brilliant white light had penetrated a dark and smoky room. I couldn't tell if what he said was true or false, but it shook my inner foundation in a way only Samson in his blind rage could have accomplished. It was from that point forward that I seriously questioned ANY person who claimed to know truth - no matter what authority they claimed. I would never again unquestioningly accept truth, merely because it had been spoken by someone who claimed specialist training or rank. From that time it seemed, I would always face persecution from the ruling status quo. And yet, Udraka continued choosing this blade of grass over that. Perhaps, he knew that he had penetrated that gossamer skin between faith and belief - perhaps not. It would take several years more, before I recognized the deception of Belief and the truth of Faith. Peter had the belief but, founded in the mind, it proved temporal.

"You've been very quiet these past few days," the Prince commented as we walked by the river. I hadn't realized what a profound affect Udraka's words had had on me.

"How can any man, little more than forty, claim to know so much?" I asked, questioning myself as much as the Prince.

"Forty!?" he exclaimed.

"Perhaps forty five?"

"My father sat on his knee as a boy," he calmly stated.

"But that would make him at least sixty?"

"Seventy five to eighty would be a closer figure."

"But he can't be... He has the skin of a young girl..."

"And his eyes?" the Prince prompted.

It was true, sometimes his dark eyes sparkled like a child, other times they held an ageless wisdom I had never seen in any other man's eyes.

"What age do you think he is then?" I asked, intrigued.

"Hard to tell," he answered choosing his words carefully. "Even the elders call him 'Old' Udraka."

The next day, I waited until Udraka began milking the Buffalo before asking. I knew he would be in a fixed position for some time and it would be hard for him to be evasive. Sitting on a low footstool with his head buried deep against the warm side of the great grey beast, he was lost in a low chant of some personal mantra.

"Udrakaji?" I started.

"You start your sentence as though you've cornered your quarry young Rabbi?" he spoke as if aware of my unspoken question. He now only called me 'Young Rabbi' when he was introducing some new information or teaching that I might find doubtful. It was as if he was saying 'Yeshuaji, what I'm about to tell you, you will disbelieve, nevertheless it's true'.

My position was clear and to not have come directly to the point, would have been dishonest.

"What year were you born?"

He suddenly laughed aloud, almost kicking over the jug of milk. The buffalo nonchalantly turned its large head to see what the commotion was all about. Indifferent, it turned away, its leathern tail sweeping across my face.

Udraka settled the buffalo with his calming hand and shook his head in amusement.

"The 'honest' question would have been - 'Udrakaji, how old are you'?" He laughed to himself and continued milking. He wasn't going to answer - and I wasn't going to leave. We both held the silence like an invisible tug-of-war. Finally he looked up from the milking and could see I was still waiting for an answer.

"What is time?" he asked directly.

I thought carefully before answering.

"Time is what is being measured between sunrise and sunset. It is what has passed between my leaving Judaea and arriving at your door," I answered, confident in my reply.

"No, it is neither. Time is separation - because you don't live in the moment. It is an illusion!"

"Separation?" I queried, never having heard it described in such a way.

"Yes. Time exists *only* because you believe you are 'separate' from anything else - and can therefore travel between these two separate things. In truth, we are all living within the vast body of God and are all intimately connected - there is no 'separation'." He smiled warmly, pleased that I had asked.

Emboldened by his reply, I went further.

"But the Torah talks of many generations of Man, how can that be, if there is no 'time'?"

Patiently, he tried to explain.

"Truth will never be found in books - not in your Torah, not even in the Vedas. Books are brought about by thought. Thought is based on memory. Memory resides in the past. Truth only exists in the moment. Without memory, thought ceases to be - so there is a fundamental dichotomy when speaking about 'truth' and 'thought' in the same breath. Truth can only be experienced directly by the heart, not by thought and the mind. Truth can only be experienced in the moment and, if we believe in 'time', we separate ourselves from that timeless wisdom of the moment."

"So we should live in an eternal moment?" I cautiously ventured.

"Exactly."

"I think I understand."

"No! Truth cannot be 'understood' or 'believed', it can only be lived." In my heart I knew what he said was true, but I didn't understand it.

As I walked away I realized he hadn't answered my question. I stopped and looked back and knew that any answer he might give, would be meaningless. His words had left me in a state of grace that didn't want the clutter of words and labels. He continued milking and I continued walking.

In all the time I spent with this gentle herb-gatherer, I never actually saw him consume anything but tea and buffalo milk. Was it possible to exist without absorbing physical food? I had learned that a direct question was worth less than the breath it took to voice it, so I decided on a different strategy. Early one morning, I woke before sunrise and left for the nearby market place. The embers of the caravan fire still glowed warm on the ground and the first camels were beginning to stir. As the darkness retreated, women arrived carrying bundles and pots. Bullocks pulled their creaking wagons, loaded with earthenware goods, sweet smelling woods and all kinds of strange foods. It was almost mid-morning by the time I saw what I had been waiting for - pomegranates! A young boy, leading a blind man, pulled a small handcart loaded with dried fruits and pomegranates. I stood back to allow them to set up their space. A brightly colored yellow silk cloth was carefully draped across the red earth and an offering was made to whatever God or Gods they looked to. Then, very specifically, the young boy laid out their produce on the ground.

"Greetings," I quietly spoke, so the blind man shouldn't be startled by my presence.

"Greetings," he replied. "It's a good day when the great Lord Vishnu sends a traveler from the land of Judaea to our humble market."

"How do you know I'm from Judaea?" I asked, amazed that a blind man could be so accurate.

He chuckled to himself as though seeing something amusing at his feet.

"It surprises you that a man with no eyes should see through you?" he laughingly taunted.

"I admit, I'm at a loss to understand how you might know."

He cocked his head to the side as though trying to see me from another angle, or listen to some unheard sound. Holding his finger upward to focus my attention, he explained.

"The sandals you wear are laced at the heal. Our local sandals are loose fitting and make a slight clicking noise when the foot is lifted from the ground. Your feet made little sound on the ground."

"Even so...," I remonstrated.

"Your clothing is made of an unbeaten fiber that hangs below your knees, brushing roughly against your body when you move. You respectfully waited until we had prepared our fruits - a local man wouldn't have," he held his hands open in offered explanation.

"And from as little as this, you're able to be so perceptive?" I asked, impressed.

"This - and the fact that everyone knows that the Great Udraka has been teaching a foreigner from Judaea," he grinned broadly. "Also, my nephew described you before you approached."

"Then you're either a rogue or a very honest man - which is it?"

"A rogue would claim to be an honest man - and an honest man, in these times, would be a rogue to claim such an honor."

"But you are a seller of fruits?"

"For those that have eyes to see I am, for those that don't, I'm a fool," he placated, in case I should think him rude for teasing a stranger. I picked up several pomegranates, flicking my fingernails against their sides to test for ripeness. He quietly listened to my efforts. He shook his head in silent denial as I tested each one.

"You don't appear to have much confidence in your own produce?" I queried.

"No sir, I have every confidence! It's just that I thought you might like the sweetest, instead of the one with most juice," he spoke, resigned to my lack of discrimination.

"Indeed, I do," I replied, taken aback by his strange and disarming manner.

"Let me," he spoke, gently leading me back so that he could approach the fruit. Again he cocked his head sideways, like a bird waiting for worms and listening to something beyond my hearing. He stood like that for some moments before crisply clapping his hands together and instantly leaning forward towards the fruit - as though expecting a response.   Then, a decision being made, his hands reached forward and picked up a small pomegranate that appeared to have less color in its skin than the others.

"This is the one," he confidently proffered.

"But it barely has any red on the outside," I protested, not entirely convinced of my ground.

"Believe me young Sir, this is the sweetest of all.   If I'm wrong, you may blacken my character with any that frequent this market," he spoke in all seriousness.

"It's too small a thing to have such serious consequence," I protested.

"My word is all I have and I have far too much respect for the Great Udraka, to embarrass his guest."   His words were solemn and meant.

"It's an extraordinary gift you have - being able to tell the sweetness of one among so many fruits, by a simple hand clap," I spoke as I handed him the coin.

"It also helps, if one finds the sweetest fruit before arriving at the market and placing it easily to hand," he mischievously smiled. The young boy tried to suppress his laughter on seeing the realization on my face.   The blind man turned his head expectantly toward the young boy.   In response, the boy gently pressed the man's hand as if to indicate I hadn't taken offense.

"In truth you are an honest rogue," I spoke to confirm I hadn't taken offense.

"There is truth and there is truth," he spoke, resignedly conceding what was apparent to everyone who knew him.

In the evening I sat at one of several tables where Udraka usually sat and listened as he spoke to some of the villagers.   There was always an abundance of food that people had donated to the great teacher in return for healings he had brought about.   The food would otherwise go to waste and there was never a shortage of mouths eager to assist in it's disposal.   Usually Udraka sat with his milk, allowing whoever wished to talk with him, the opportunity to approach.

"When you invite people to your table," he spoke looking around the table, "don't invite your friends, your brothers or your wealthy neighbor.   Invite the poor, the crippled, the lame and the blind. You will be blessed because they can't repay you - God will pay their bill."

Udraka provided more food than was visible on the table. People left his table with a happy heart and a soul that yearned for talk of higher matters.   When he stopped talking, I put forward the pomegranate and told him how I had come to have it.

"Ashoka," he spoke with a smile.   "Yes, I've seen him in the market place since ... for many years."

"I still don't know if he placed this in a specific position before I approached, or if he really does have some inner gift."   I spoke, hoping that Udraka might be able to throw some light on the subject.

"Does it matter?" he answered.

"I'd simply like to know," I responded.

"Was there magic in the moment?" he asked with a challenging smile.

"Yes," I reluctantly answered.

"Then be satisfied."

He could see that his answer didn't satisfy my young curiosity, so thought for a moment before elaborating.

"A thousand years ago, a wise man sat in a beautiful valley. Beside him, sat a fool. Both, did nothing. The difference being that where the fool did nothing, the wise man left nothing undone."   As he spoke, he split the hard skin of the fruit against the side of the table. The darkest red juice ran between his fingers, which he caught on his outstretched tongue, pointedly looking into my eyes.

"Does that answer your question?"

He wasn't referring to Ashoka.   As if to emphasize his point, he took a huge and unnecessary bite out of the fruit, before handing the other half to me. Taking a bite, I found it really was the sweetest pomegranate I had ever tasted. Udraka smiled.

"So which is he?" I asked in need of an answer.

"For that, you'd have to sit in a valley with him," he spoke. Placing the responsibility for the answer squarely back on my shoulders.

"The need for answers comes from the mistaken belief that the world isn't perfect, Yeshua. To know the world *is* perfect, is to see that God is everywhere."

"But I see so much poverty everywhere, how can you say God is everywhere?" I asked.

"Your *experience* is that there is poverty. The truth is, God chooses to experience itself in such a way. By judging it to be poverty, you separate yourself from the experience of being." He left his words to work their magic as he turned to a villager who had come to present his new-born child for a blessing.

"Have you visited the caves yet, Yeshuaji?" he abruptly asked, though still talking with the family of the new-born.

"Which caves?" I asked.

"That way," he pointed to the West. "You should. You'll find it interesting." He immediately turned away and returned to his conversation in progress. Udraka never made suggestions lightly and for him to say I *should* visit the caves - I could barely wait for dawn to break.

Before daylight, I headed West. After several hours of walking up into the mountains I saw the opening of a large cave, from which several women emerged. Wearing brightly colored Saris and coming out of the darkness of the cave, they appeared like exotic flowers opening to the morning's first rays.

At the entrance to the cave, small stone carvings of Hindu deities were placed in naturally occurring niches. Brightly colored vegetable dyes ran down the rocks from where devotees had placed small offerings of food. I moved expectantly forward. Deep inside the cave, where the daylight barely penetrated, I came across the naked Baba. His long matted tresses were tied above his head in a huge top-knot. He appeared a youth, perhaps a few years older than myself. At his waist, a thin cord hung down from which his flaccid penis was suspended in an upright position. The palms of both hands were held together at his chest in the usual manner of Hindu greeting. He stood motionless, his eyes half-closed in meditation and facing a curious but natural rock formation. The formation seemed to have grown up from the ground and appeared in the form of a two foot high penis. Garlands of orange flowers hung around the base and a musky scent hung in the air. I watched for several hours as pilgrims came to pay their respects. This was perhaps one of the most extraordinary sights I had ever seen. The pilgrims paid their silent homages, extending themselves fully prostrate on the ground: first towards the rock and then towards this standing and naked Baba. He never gave any indication of acknowledgment. Several women approached, prostrating themselves fully and then standing up where their hands had reached to, then again lying down; so that after about ten prostrations, they reached the feet of the Baba. At this point the women pulled back the shawls from their heads and, leaning forward, lightly kissed the Baba's flaccid penis. The act was carried out with total devotion and held no suggestion of sexuality.

"A Shivite," Udraka explained when I asked him. "He was worshipping the Linga - that rock."

"What is a Linga?" I asked, surprised that he should take my adventure so calmly.

"It appears as the male reproductive organ and is a representative symbol of Unmanifested Divinity - the potential creativity of God."

"How do they occur?" I asked about the rock.

"Some are natural formations of minerals dripping from the ceilings, forming deposits over the centuries," he answered leaving another question hanging.

"- And the others?" I asked.

"Some say they are Divinely created," he flatly answered.

"What do you say?" I pointedly asked.

"I don't worship the Linga," was all he would say, neither affirming or denying the practice.

"I understand the prostrations - there's nothing new in that, but..." Udraka smiled at the sensitivity of the issue.

"They are helping the Baba achieve Nirvana," he explained. "He has achieved a level beyond the senses. By restraint and regulation of breath, he is focusing his creative fluids so that they are transmuted into Prana - the essential energy of life."

"Sexual energy into Spirit?" I suggested.

"Exactly. The Prana, or life force, can then enter the spinal column and feed the chakras - the spiritual energy centers. The devotees were assisting him focus his attention in the physical world while allowing him to see that he had transcended this most physical need."

"Is this necessary to achieve God Consciousness?" From the way I asked, he could tell that I wasn't overly convinced.

"Necessary? No, it isn't necessary," he answered patiently. "A washer woman down by the river, could achieve the same - if she saw her task as being as sacred as the Baba views his."

It was at this time that I learned about Raja Yoga and the raising of Kundalini. "Coiled around the base of the spine, is a sleeping dragon," Udraka had said. "Through the use of rhythmic breathing and concentrated thought, this dragon can be made to wake. When it does, it soars up the spine, energizing the subtle rotations of energy we call Chakras. Each Chakra holds within it metaphysical gifts and super-conscious abilities."

"What sort of abilities?" I cautiously inquired.

"The gift of Prophecy, clairvoyance - the ability to align directly with the will of God," he answered as if shedding a considerable burden. It seemed almost as if he had been waiting for me just to ask that question.

I spent six years living in the caves of Jagganath. There I met many men whose consciousness had little root in these lower worlds. Many had caused the Kundalini energy to rise up the spine through unnatural methods and had paid the price. Indeed, some of these poor souls stole food from the wild animals and were as wretched as any I have ever known. Others taught me about powerful elemental forces that man can call to his own use and the cost showed darkly in their souls. What contrast those dark caves were to the time I had spent with the Jains! One of the most important lessons I learned was that, although these men worshipped countless deities, they were all different aspects of the One God. Each worshipped that aspect of God with which they most easily identified. For me, it emphasized that *everything* in creation is a manifestation of God.

"All Gods *are* different aspects of the same God," Udraka confirmed. "Unfortunately, over time, the different sects forget this and start to claim that their's is the only true reflection of the Ultimate Source. How can you claim one facet of a diamond is more important than another? Each is essential and serves the whole. When each facet claims to be the originator, then all suffer. That's a sure sign that an Avatar, or World Teacher, is about to come into incarnation - to restore the truth to common knowledge."

It was at this time I was taught Kriya Yoga. Every morning before sunrise I joined a group of locals down by the river. Several Yogis came and went, each teaching his own particular knowledge of the Heart. First, we were taught the Asanas - the physical postures that strengthen and align the Physical, Emotional and Spiritual bodies. Once these were mastered we were taught how to express these inner energies outwardly, through the Heart Chakra. Many healings were brought about by the practitioners. Often villagers would come with their illness' and have the practitioners lay their hands on them. The Yogis showed us how to achieve the healings, though never participated themselves.

"There is no need", one Yogi explained.

"Then why do we do it?", I had asked.

"Because you need to experience God working through you", he had answered.

"And you don't?" I pressed.

"I *am* God", he had answered without any trace of ego. "You have yet to know this." His words had the most profound effect on me. He hadn't claimed to be the unique Creator, he was simply claiming not to be separate from that totality of consciousness we refer to as God.

I recall one night walking along the banks of a silent and silvered river. The reflection of the moon rippled in the inky darkness. Ahead, small fires sat huddled against the dark and the wonderful smell of sandalwood traced the edges of my nose. Dark figures moved against the still darker night. Occasionally the figures were illuminated by a sudden crackle and showering sparks from the fires. As I stood, unseen in the shadows, I suddenly sensed a figure standing beside me. Startled, I turned to find a tall naked man with matted hair that hung in loose ropes down to just below his knees. Grey ash covered his entire body and three red lines were daubed across his forehead.

"Death or life?" he spat without looking at me. He was a head taller than me and would, under normal circumstances, have presented a forbidding figure. Somehow I sensed no threat from him.

"Death or life?" he repeated, still not looking toward me.

"I don't understand?"

"What you see." He indicated towards the scene ahead. Five figures tended several funeral pyres. The central portion of one pyre collapsed under the licking flame and the naked body assumed an almost seated position as though surveying it's funereal assistants going about their work. One of the attendants using a fly whisk sprinkled water from an upturned human skull that hung from his waist. The attendants looked in the direction of the gazing and eyeless corpse, towards myself and my companion. We were still too far from them to pick us out in the dark. They returned to their immediate duties at hand.

"Who are you that asks me?"

"Why, do you fear answering a stranger?" he gruffly answered.

"I have certain expectations when walking at night in strange lands" I cautiously answered.

"Then it's Death you see," he answered emphatically and with a certain knowing satisfaction.

"How can you say that? I'm stranger to you sir."

"Death isn't a stranger to me. I wear death," he indicated the grey ash covering his body.

"Then, please explain," I spoke, standing a little distance away.

"Again, you speak from death. You want to remain in the known and anything that is known is dead to the moment. The mind is a mouse that chases it's tail, hoping never to seize it's prey. If it ever did catch the tail, it would recognize self chasing self - a futile existence."

"Self is futile?" I queried.

"It can't exist without limitation. Therefore how can it comprehend the limitless being of Shiva, the totality of God," he spoke breaking off into uncontrolled laughter at the simplicity of this evident truth.

"Perhaps, I answered from mind, so that Shiva might be able to experience itself in the cleverness of your words?" I cautiously ventured. The man appeared thunderstruck and then, again laughed as though his sides would split.

"I walked into my own tiger trap," he spoke between hysterical laughter.

"And what kind of a tiger is this, that has trapped itself?"

"Ramanath Giri - a Sadhu. And how may I know you young stranger that stalks the home of the dead?"

"My name is Yeshua of the house of Joseph."

"Then, Yeshua of the house of Joseph, what you see before you is the face of God," he again indicated the funeral pyre.

"I see only life grieving for what has parted."

"Life serves death, under the illusion that there is separation."

"And for you there is no separation?" I asked.

He paused for a moment as though a chasm had opened up before us. He narrowed his eyes and crouched close to the ground, sniffing before answering.

"I know there are other tiger traps close by and only my Guru knows the straight path," he mischievously smiled, aware his ego might again, be on shifting ground.

"I'd like to meet your Guru - if that's possible," I tentatively asked.

"He's gone to Kailash."

"The mountain home of Lord Shiva?"

He nodded, impressed that I, a stranger in his land, should know about the mountain vastness deep in the Himalayas.

He considered a moment before speaking.

"We'll meet here at dawn and I'll give you his answer." With that, almost unconsciously, he urinated directly ahead and ran off towards the grouped fires.

For some hours I watched the silvered darkness of the river make it's stately passage towards the sea. Occasionally a log, or the bloated body of a dead dog, broke the tranquil surface. There was a timelessness about India I haven't seen in any other land. Here, there seemed no place for effort. Even the poverty I saw all around, appeared chosen rather than imposed. Only the cows held an air of innocence as they ambled through the alleyways and attempted to help themselves to market trader's produce, so carefully laid out on the handcarts. The people had a tolerance for the animals as they gently chided and guided them on their way. There was a dawning here for me. Almost tangibly I felt that I stood before a large curtained theater from which the curtains were about to be drawn. Did this strange Sadhu have something to do with this curious quality of tangible intangibility?

"It's time," the Sadhu spoke, again suddenly appearing at my side. The sun had not yet risen, but a warm orange light already etched the underside of the distant clouds. Following a path along the river bank, we walked in silence for more than an hour, leaving all traces of civilization behind us. Finally, we came across a stark and single tree that leaned out of a huge sand dune. The tree grew at such an angle, it looked as though it would fall at any minute. Among the sparse leaves, small birds weaved pendulous and intricate nests that hung limply from the pale-limbed branches. As we approached, the birds flew off like a cloud of insects caught in the evening breeze. At the foot of the tree, motionless, sat an old man, naked and cross-legged. In front of him, wisps of smoke rose from the burning embers at his feet. The fireplace was completely tidy and three feet square. Around the edges of the smoldering square, fresh marigolds lay carefully arranged. Perhaps three pieces of wood smoldered at their hearts while the grey ashes around, lay flat and carefully tended.   The Guru himself held his right arm pointed directly upward, beside his head.   Although the man was painfully thin, his raised arm was nothing less than emaciated.   The finger nails of his right hand had grown so long that they curled grotesquely back towards his palm.   The nails on his middle and forth fingers had actually intertwined.   A feeling of disgust ran though me..

"Babaji has had his arm pointing to God for twenty eight years," he spoke kindly, as if reading my thoughts.   "It is my joy to attend to his every need."

"Why?" I asked, incredulous.

"Why?" he answered, surprised at my ignorance.   "When he was a young boy, Babaji promised to carry out this penance, if God

41

would reveal his true face." The Sadhu looked with awed love towards the strange figure sitting in front of the fire.

"How long will he hold his arm up?"

"Until he no longer sees the face of God in his inner vision."

"Will he speak to me?" I dubiously asked, seeing that the old man had his eyes closed and was in a deep trance.

The Sadhu indicated for me to be seated on one side of the fire while he sat on the other. Without lowering his voice, he continued speaking.

"Babaji is at Kailash, but I sent word that you were coming," he spoke, while retrieving a small two-sided rattle drum from behind the Guru. Without a further word he closed his eyes and, while reciting mantras, rapidly twisted the drum with his wrist. By his action, two attached balls of leather alternately struck either side of the drum. At first I couldn't detect any specific rhythm. Gradually the drum created an overtone with the chanted mantra, such that there became little distinction between the instrument and the voice. I closed my eyes and felt my body begin to sway with the hypnotic rhythm.

"It has taken you a long time to come and visit your old friend, Yeshu," the Guru suddenly spoke. After several hours of sitting listening to the Sadhu chanting, I was startled by the suddenness of this clear and resonant voice.

"With respect, I think you're mistaken. I've only recently arrived in this land," I answered, confused. The Guru's eyes were the most piercing blue - rare enough for someone from Judaea, but unheard of for anyone from India. The Sadhu remained with his eyes shut and gently placed the drum down at his side. The Guru lowered his right arm and reached for the jar of water beside him. Stopping his action on seeing my surprise, he offered me the water before drinking himself.

"Your arm!" I spoke, horrified.

"It's nothing," he casually dismissed. "A little sore perhaps."

I drank from the wooden and brass jar. To my surprise, the water was cool and sweet.

"You have traveled so far. What is it you wish to know," he spoke as if my question were of greater importance than the breaking of his penance.

"What is my true purpose, Babaji," I asked, not seriously expecting any great insight. After all, what could an old man who points at the sky for twenty-eight years possibly know of the world or its affairs? He smiled, as if reading my thoughts.

"Your true purpose, Yeshu of the house of Joseph, cannot be revealed by me - at this time. I can only speak for the time you spend in this land."

"I'd be honored to know."

"Your purpose in this land, is to see beyond the world of Duality - beyond good and evil," he spoke with unshakable certainty.

"I'm not sure I understand. Are you saying that there is no good and no evil?"

He smiled before answering. "How easily we forget," he spoke as though it was something I should already know.

"There is no good and there is no evil," he continued. "There is only the face of God. I may call it Shiva, Vishnu, Brahma - or even Yahweh!"

"Then what is the true name of God?" I tentatively asked.

"To name the Totality is to separate our consciousness from it. It is meaningless. The Totality simply is." He could see my confusion, so continued. "To name a sunset is to separate ourselves from the Totality that is expressing itself through our heart. The mind is the great labeler, but has little bearing on reality."

"Like a single wave believing itself to be the ocean?"

He considered for some moments before speaking again. "The Ocean of Consciousness is like the still mind, before the wind of thought. As the external element of wind plays upon the surface, the wave gains a consciousness of being separate from the ocean. Man is like that wave - believing himself to be in anyway separate from the vast Ocean of Love we call God." He waved expansively as if to demonstrate his point. Suddenly I became aware of just how cold it was. Taking my eyes from his, I looked around at the cold mountain vastness. The tree beneath which we had been sitting, and the flowing river - were nowhere to be seen. Instead, as far as the eye could see, rugged snow-capped mountains lay like a soft carpet at our feet.

Abruptly I opened my eyes. The Sadhu still sat across from me, with his eyes shut in meditation. The Guru still sat cross-legged with his arm raised towards the sky. A faint smile played at the corner of his lips. Darkness was beginning to fall so I got up to leave.

For many days after, I was deeply disturbed by the experience with the Guru. Had it been an illusion? Had I succumbed to the smell of the aromatic wood, so carefully tended as if it were a garden? Did it really matter that I should know? At the deepest part of me, I felt the Guru's words were true. My mind was like that single wave, being tossed here and there. At the conscious level I needed to know, yet an echo that lay darkly at the back of my head, whispered that the truth was to be lived, not understood.

It was at the Prince's suggestion that I visited the Ashram of Tyagi Baba.

"He has a reputation I've never heard falter," he said. "It's said he is close to God and has shown many followers the way."

"Followers" I asked, unintentionally letting slip a certain disdain in my voice.

"Yeshua, a follower here in India, is not what you may be accustomed to in the West," he gently chided. "Here the Guru looks on himself as the servant of all. The 'followers' try to make the Guru's path to God as painless as possible. They take care of the daily tasks that might otherwise distract the Guru from his communion with God."

"- And the followers?"

"They hope to obtain Moksha - liberation from earthly illusion, by being in the presence of someone who has direct contact with God."

"Like the heart and the head - without one, the other has no existence," I ventured, hoping not to offend the beliefs of the Prince's homeland.

"In a way," he answered, unconvinced. "Though you make no mention of devotion. To the follower, the Guru is the embodiment of God in this physical world. His prime motivation is his love for the Guru. In the West, I saw much fear of being denounced by your 'holy' men. The Rabbis even deliver death pronouncements on followers that don't follow the 'Law'."

"What you say is true, sweet Prince. We've been taught a vengeful God, a God who is to be feared. It's never sat well with me that the priests tell us to sacrifice life, so that we should honor our God."

"Can you explain to me why Abraham should sacrifice his only son in order to prove his greater love for God," he carefully asked, equally eager not to offend my beliefs?

"Now you find me in the desert with no camel - I have no answer," I smiled. This was one of the central issues I had never understood. "We were taught that it showed Abraham had a greater love for God than for those he held most dear." The Prince remained silent so that I was forced to say more. "I'd like to say that these words echo in my heart, but in truth I see the ground is stained dark around the base of my water carrier." He laughed and my spirit felt lighter.

"Yeshua ben Joseph, you have spent too much time with Ashoka. You'll either be a great spiritual leader - or a politician! This land has no need of more spiritual leaders, but a politician could go far?"

"If I was a politician, I'd tax every man who claimed to know truth."

"Then only the children would escape taxation!" he laughed.

"But of course - they would be our spiritual leaders!" We both laughed, feeling a childlike kinship.

We walked for several hours before arriving at the small grouping of huts that were Tyagi Baba's Ashram. Several water-buffalo waded through the muddy fields, pulling their wooden ploughs. Behind them, slim men gently cajoled the animals, constantly urging the great beasts forward. Most of the mud-baked huts surrounded a central threshing area, where several women tossed grains into the air before catching them again in their broad flat baskets. Facing the threshing yard sat the rotund figure of Tyagi Baba. He sat, shaded beneath a crude awning of banana leaves and palm fronds.   His gaze appeared unseeing and directed forward. The Prince walked into his direct line of sight, but Tyagi Baba gave no indication of recognizing him, or anything else in his field of vision.   On seeing us, one of the women smiled and ushered us around the edge of the threshing ground, to be seated at the side of her Guru.   Without changing the direction of his gaze, the Guru almost imperceptibly bowed his head forward, the only acknowledgment of our presence.

Two cups of piping hot Chai were presented by a little boy, who also informed us that Tyagi Baba wouldn't be able to talk with us for four days.   Again the Guru leaned imperceptibly forward, as if to confirm the boy's words.   We remained only long enough to drink the tea.

"Buffalo milk," the Prince stated as I inquired about the smoothness of the Guru's glowing skin.   "From the age of twelve, he hasn't touched food or water - only Buffalo milk."

"Why was he unable to speak with us?   He knew we were there," I asked.

"He knew we were there," the Prince repeated.   "Sometimes these wise men like to present us with enigmas, so that we might learn how to ask the right questions."

"Or, he may have been preparing for a ceremony...?"

"Which we may have interrupted if he had spoken," he finished, nodding in agreement that that was the more likely.

Four days later we found ourselves traveling back towards the Ashram.   It was late evening when we arrived and some kind of festival was underway.   Where the threshing area had been, a bonfire was in its later stages.   Where the Guru had previously sat, lay a garland of purple Hibiscus flowers, formally arranged on the ground.   The fire again lay carefully tended.   No stray pieces of wood extended beyond the grey ash and glowing embers.   Six musicians kept up a pulsating cacophony of disjointed sound, while the villagers, dressed in full-length white robes held close at the ankles, spun like the Dervishes of the Caspian.   With one open hand extended to the sky and the other to the ground, the dancers endlessly rotated on the balls of their left feet.   Despite the disunity of the music, the dancers kept a regular beat as though they maintained one breath.

"Where is Tyagi Baba?" the Prince asked an onlooker. The man looked at him with disdain.

"It's the festival of the Phoenix," he spoke as though the answer were self evident.

"We are strangers," I interrupted.

"Then you are most fortunate," he spoke with envy in his voice, which seemed to belie his words. He turned back to the festivities, leaving the Prince and I wondering at his words.

Long into the night, the fire burned and the dancers danced. No further wood was added to the flickering flames and eventually all that remained were the embers. Then, as if by some unspoken instruction, the dancers and musicians stopped in unison. Forming a line at one end of the fire, they waited. Solemnly, an aged man, shaved bald and dressed in saffron robes, approached. Collecting the garland of Hibiscus flowers, he carefully handed one flower to each of the dancers. With this, each dancer leaned forward to received some brief and whispered message from the old teacher. Once every devotee had received his flower, they each slowly walked across the hot and glowing ground; the sparks flying up from their heels. Some even carried glowing embers between their toes after leaving the pit, yet seemed unaware of any apparent pain. They appeared to be in a state of ecstasy, their gaze returning to the embers.

"The festival of the Phoenix?" I queried, looking towards the fire-walkers. The Prince shrugged his shoulders, as mystified as myself. We looked around but there was still no sign of the Guru. Whatever kept him from the festivities, it must have been of some importance. Gradually the curious onlookers from the village drifted back towards the village, further down the hill. Those that wished to remain, were politely urged to leave. We also prepared to depart, but the elderly teacher who had handed out the flowers, indicated we should specifically stay. The dancers sat down, cross-legged and gazed into the few remaining embers.

As dawn approached, I became aware of a low resonant chant - so low that at first I distrusted my own hearing. I looked to the devotees, particularly to their throat muscles, but couldn't detect any specific movement that might be generating this sound.

"You hear that?" I asked the Prince.

"Nothing," he shrugged.

"Like a deep humming - a human voice?"

"Nothing," he repeated.

As he spoke, two white-clad devotees, carried forward a large water container. The bald saffron-robed teacher spoke a few words of prayer while the two assistants busied themselves with a large water-melon. The melon was cut into two halves and then the inner flesh removed. Then, an elaborately carved wooden pitch-fork was ceremoniously thrust into the outer shells. Using a stringed carrier, the two empty casings were then suspended from a yoke.

After both the casings had been submerged in the water-carrier, two men, for whom it was evidently great honor, stepped forward. All those gathered, sat in total silence while the two young men, walking either side of the embers, doused the almost dormant cinders, the water sprinkling from the pitch-fork holes. Strangely they took care for the water not to pool and not to sprinkle too much in any one spot. Still I heard that low resonant chant.

Once it was seen that no heat remained in the doused fire, several men began removing the darkened earth to reveal the moisture-darkened soil beneath. They dug intently, but without undue concern. At one end of the pit, a gently inclining ramp began to form until the depth reached the chest of the diggers. The lead digger beckoned towards the old teacher. He came to make a closer inspection. From where I sat, I could see that they had come across a slab of rock, which appeared to be resting on two buried and horizontal tree trunks. Two harnessed bullocks were brought to the edge of the incline and ropes attached to the slab.

Now, although the sound I had heard earlier was no louder, in some strange way it sounded clearer.

"Don't you hear it?" I asked.

"Still nothing," the Prince answered, disappointed.

Using a rope through the noses of the large beasts, a young boy urged the bullocks forward. At first attempt, the slab refused to move. The bullocks complained, as though they had already estimated the size of the task and, in all fairness, they needed help. With a sharp twist of the lead rope, the bullocks again lurched forward. This time the earth around the slab loosened, to the evident relief of the onlookers. On the third attempt, the slab eased forward along the tree trunks. From a shout from one of the devotees, the bullocks were halted, while the man jumped into the pit and relieved some obstructing debris. A look from some of the others suggested he had over-stepped his authority. Moments later, the slab emerged from the pit and was dragged off to a nearby field. Moving closer, I could see a saffron-clad body, laying in the ground between the two tree trunks.

"Tyagi Baba," the old teacher spoke, standing beside us.

"He died?" the Prince asked, surprised.

The old man simply smiled and invited us closer. The earth that had fallen on the shrouded body lay still and ominous. I looked to the old teacher - he seemed unconcerned. The young boy who had previously brought us the Chai, cautiously jumped into the pit. Dusting away the dirt from the saffron shroud, he was anything but, unconcerned. The boy looked upward to the old man, hoping to be relieved of his present duty, but without success. The old man urged him on. The boy carefully unfolded part of the shroud to reveal the face of his beloved Guru. There was no sign of life in the face, but he appeared unblemished and in a deep sleep.

At a signal from the old man, four men entered the pit and carefully carried the body to where the stone slab now rested. The body was slightly inclined so that the face should receive the first rays of the morning sun. Almost roughly, it seemed to me, plugs of wax were removed from the Guru's nostrils and ears. Everyone waited. Suddenly the body jerked as though a large weight had struck the chest. The eyelids quivered before opening to reveal only the whites of the eye. Slowly the irises drifted down from some position they had been focused on high in the head. A look of frenzy gradually faded to one of peace.

The Guru's body was then laid naked while heated oils were carefully massaged into the motionless muscles and joints. It was at this point I understood what the Prince had tried to explain about the devotion of 'followers'. I had seen adulation from 'followers' before, but never this selfless devotion. Uncalled for and totally unexpected, I felt tears of happiness roll down my cheeks.

As the sun's rays warmed the ground, the muscles of the body eased and the chest gently began to expand with breath. The old teacher stood close by the head of his Guru as full consciousness began to return. The Guru's eyes opened and, on meeting the old teacher's, widened - as if in signal. The teacher quickly thrust his fingers into the mouth of the Guru and hooked his tongue forward. The Guru gasped a lungful of air, as one who might have swum up from the deepest waters. The devotees continued kneading his muscles, until the fingers of the Guru's right hand slightly raised, requesting them to stop. A warm blanket was placed over the body. Again the Guru made eye contact with the old teacher as though communicating some unspoken command. The devotees were waved away, while we were beckoned forward. I'll never forget how that prone figure that had been buried deep in the earth, made direct eye contact with me. An electric charge ran through my entire body and again I heard that low resonant sound. The effect was strangely blinding. All my field of vision could take in, was the golden light that seemed to radiate from the Guru's half-closed eyes. My body felt to be inwardly burning. Time seemed to stretch out limitlessly before me, yet it may have only been seconds.

The next thing I recall, was the Prince slapping me gently around the face. I had passed out.

"Yeshua, are you all right?" he asked, seriously concerned.

He helped me into a seated position.

"Yes, I think so." Dazed as I was, I answered to calm him.

"He will be fully recovered in a few days." I looked to see who had spoken. It was Guru Tyagi Baba. He sat upright on the stone slab, totally unconcerned or even elated at his own recovery.

"It's not every day that the dead are raised," he lightly joked as if it were of little consequence.

"Forgive me," I uttered, unsure of what to say or even how to behave under such extraordinary circumstances. In a sense, I felt embarrassed that I should faint where he had been buried alive; yet I probably looked the worse for my experience than he did.

"No need," he lightly offered. He waited to be certain I was recovered. "Is your name Jesus?"

"In the Greek tongue, that is what I'm called," I answered.

"Can you prove it?" he asked.

It seemed such a bizarre question from a person who less than an hour earlier, had lain as a corpse beneath the burning ground.

"Prove it?" I stupidly repeated.

"Yes, prove it," he gently repeated.

Confused, I looked to the Prince, who was equally confused.

"The Prince here will confirm it," I stated without conviction. Inwardly I knew this wasn't what was required. Immediately I found myself speaking words that I hadn't consciously formed.

"When you were beneath the ground, I heard the sound of God echoing in your heart." The Prince stood back, surprised at my words. Though I didn't understand my own statement, I knew it was true.

"Then you really are Jesus. I have a message for you," he spoke looking around and indicating that everyone else should withdraw. The saffron-robed elder lead the Prince away. Before leaving, the Prince looked to see that I was well. I smiled to dispel any concerns he might have. The Guru waited until we were alone.

"Have you heard of the Vairagi's, Jesusji?" he spoke affectionately. I indicated I hadn't, so he continued. "They're an ancient order of Elder Brothers. Though they are detached from wordly desires, their influence still guides our highest aspirations." He looked to see that I was following before continuing.

"They are of the world, but not in it. To many, they appear ageless - and I don't merely mean hundreds of years."

"Where do they live?" I asked, barely able to contain my excitement. He smiled at my enthusiasm as he gestured broadly around him.

"Their bodies are maintained in places inaccessible to most mortals. Even if people were to stumble across their cities, they wouldn't be seen by the eye - unless invited," he solemnly spoke.

"How would...?" I hesitated in finishing the question.

"How would you be invited? That I can't answer. When you truly comprehend what you are asking, then you will have your answer."

"Have you been?" I asked, throwing caution to the wind.

"Invited is not a word I might use - 'taken' would be more appropriate," he smiled.

"Against your will?" I asked, concerned.

He paused several moments before answering. "There isn't an easy answer to your question. What I may consider *my* will on this lower physical level, may be entirely different from my soul's purpose. So, if my feet decide to go this way and my head decides to go the other, my head is likely to get the casting vote!"

"But you said - 'taken'?"

"You ask me to speak of things for which this lower world has no language, therefore I use such a crude word. When a person is able to raise his vibration to a similar frequency to the Vairagi Masters, then they *may* step into your consciousness. This is largely how they communicate. Others appear in the outer world and influence great leaders - until they are recognized. They are not known to history - at least not what is taught in the outer world."

"Do any move in the outer world now?" I hesitantly asked.

He looked directly at me. "There has never been a time when they haven't been among us," he spoke so finally that I felt I had asked too much. He clearly didn't want to speak further about his personal experience.

"You mentioned, you had a message?" I asked, hoping I hadn't over-stepped my position. A beaming smile broke across his face.

"Yes, indeed! As you heard the sound of God, I was 'taken' to be with our Elder Brothers so that I could bring you this message. *'Jesus the Nazarene, when you have found the courage of a lion and a mother's love - embodied in stone - then you will know your true purpose.*" He fell silent so that his words would be etched in my heart.

I had absolutely no idea what he meant, but I had received my cue to leave.

The Prince and I walked home in silence. I so wanted to tell him all I had been told, but knew that at my deepest level I was bound to silence. The Prince was too true a friend to even inquire. He trusted that if there were anything he should know, I would tell him. Through my whole life I don't think I had a truer friend.

Something had happened that night. It wasn't just the extraordinary experience with Guru Tyagi Baba, it was something far less tangible but further reaching. The molecules of my body felt to be in a curious state of agitation. It wasn't so much uncomfortable, as a realignment. Whatever this enigmatic message was, it resonated with my body in a way that confirmed my unknown destiny.

"What is a Mehla?" I asked the Prince one day.

"A meeting", he answered. "Why do you ask?"

"I've heard it mentioned several times and people seem to regard it with awe".

"Oh, *that* Mehla," he spoke, his eyes flashing with delight.

"What is it?" I asked, intrigued by his response.

"You mean the Kumbha Mehla," he responded as if he were about to deliver a surprise present.

"Yes, Kumbha Mehla - that's it!"

He pursed his lips slightly, as he always did when about to deliver good news.

"The 'Kumbha' Mehla is a vast meeting of Spiritual teachers that takes place once very twelve years," he began. "It's the most important Spiritual festival to take place in the whole of India. Even ascetics that live in isolated mountain caves attend the Mehla. It only takes place when all the planets are in a propitious alignment."

"What's the purpose of this Mehla?" I asked.

"It's like a vast initiation. Millions attend. The purpose is hard to explain. It's as though every one's Spiritual vibration is increased, simply by attending."

"How has it come about?" I asked.

"Legend tells that the Gods fought over a pot of Divine Nectar and that four drops of nectar fell to earth. Where the drops fell, the earth was sanctified and now these places are the most divine locations in the physical world. It's here that the Mehlas are held in rotation. I attended one ten years ago and it was the most incredible experience of my life."

"In what way?" I asked, never having seen the Prince quite this open or animated.

"It gave me a glimpse into higher dimensions that I never even dreamed existed. My body seemed to be filled with light for weeks after the festival".

"Did it leave a lasting effect?" I asked in wonder.

"It did. Udraka likened it to the turtle: when the turtle first breaks the surface of the water, very little of it is seen. Then, with only the slightest movement, a large shell is exposed. The Mehla is like that slight movement. I seemed to have a greater comprehension of how everything in the Universe is intimately connected. Before, I had had the understanding - from listening to many Gurus; now I have the 'knowing'." He smiled, his enthusiasm eclipsing his natural modesty.

"I'd like to attend?" I ventured. The Prince's expression immediately changed to serious reserve.

"I don't think that would be advisable" he respectfully stated.

"Why?" I asked, disappointed. The Prince was hesitant in answering, but saw I wasn't going to allow his statement to pass.

"Because the teachers enter into public debate - and many reputations have been destroyed," he finally answered. "The whole of India will know of any failure."

"Then I have no choice - I will attend!"

For two years we traveled and met extraordinary men and wonderful teachers. Those that had the most to teach, were the most generous and, by their living example I understood, that to receive, one must first give. This is an inexorable truth. Those that hid behind mysticism and vague suggestion of profundity had the least to impart, though they mostly believed themselves to have the most.

At the age of twenty four I found myself traveling towards India's most profound festival - the Kumbha Mehla, being held at Benares. As we traveled beside the great river Ganges, I could sense the veneration the people held towards their 'Great Mother'. At first light, people submerged their bodies along its banks for cleansing. Funeral pyres burned or smoldered incessantly, while large black birds pecked at the discarded bodies of the poor. It wasn't uncommon to see smaller birds settling on bloated torsos as they slowly made their way down towards the sea. 'Resting in the arms of our Great Mother' was how they described it. As we neared Benares, the aged sat with their backs to the river, so that when they took their last breaths, they could fall in full consciousness backwards into the arms of their waiting Goddess. Never have I seen such children, who looked on death as easily as they looked on life. Death didn't appear taboo - not something to be feared. And those that weren't sick - of which there were untold numbers, had a shine in their dark eyes as if they held a secret - a knowing. More than anything, it was the children of India that impressed me most. They had an open smile that appeared to know more of me than I knew about myself. The closer we came to the sacred city, the more the flow of people grew - like mountain streams to a crystal lake. The Great Debate or Kumbha Mehla as they called it, was only days away. The moon was almost full and the tension in the air was tangible. Many of the great spiritual leaders would falter at this debate - perhaps, myself included. I felt I had little choice. I needed to hear what the greatest spiritual minds had to say. I was driven to speak. It wasn't that I had anything specific to say, only that something within me needed to be immersed in truth - and merely being an observer at the debate wouldn't satisfy that inner fire. I had an anxiety which I didn't recognize as foreboding.

The huge temples of Benares were inspirational in themselves. These buildings hadn't been built by forced labor. To me, it appeared that every brick had been laid with love. Each had been tenderly settled. It was the first time I had seen buildings that emitted bright auras. Pale iridescent light played at their edges, reflecting the love that had been put into their construction. After my training with the Yogis, I was perfectly able to read a person's aura, but rarely did. For the Yogis it was a method of gauging another's spirituality. I felt it would be a spiritual intrusion and only ever did this, if asked by the person whose aura I was to read. Buildings and rocks were entirely different. Apart from naturally occurring crystals, stones could be made to absorb and then re-emit their own vibrations and spiritual aspirations. Walking through the busy streets of Benares was like receiving an inner massage through unseen, though never-the-less, real color.   That's not to say I never saw malice or greed.   Many 'so-called' spiritual Masters displayed their credentials openly, little realizing how they created an insurmountable gulf between themselves and their devotees.   Many rode fabulous palanquins on top of gaudily painted elephants.   As if that weren't enough, one I saw, was lead by two hundred armed devotees - all carrying various exotic wind instruments that must have seen active service at the walls of Jericho!   The raucous sound scattered livestock and caused many to flee for their homes.   They reminded me very much of the Men in Black that controlled our Temple.

"Do you like it?" the Prince shouted above the wailing sounds.

"Very interesting," I smiled back.

"Yes Yeshua, politics may be your destiny," he joked at my non-committal.

"It's a beautiful city," I shouted as we were carried forward in the dense crowd.   For a time I lost sight of the Prince.   At one place the street narrowed and the crowd continue to surge forward.   The human congestion was such that my shoulders were actually in pain. Several women passed out under the crush and were trampled underfoot.   Caught up in the crowd were four water-buffalo. Normally docile, the huge creatures now stampeded in panic.   One even mounted another, trying to escape and fell sideways onto a group of children, killing them outright.   Several people were gored on the horns through no animosity of the animals, but in blind threshing terror.   Suddenly I was seized by three men who dragged me out of the main flow of the crowd.   I had heard of the followers of Kali, who abducted foreigners visiting the Great festivals and fully expected to feel a knife at my throat.   One of the men, who was quite blind in one eye, smiled a toothless grin as he dragged me forward, causing me to fall heavily against some stone steps.   Falling loose from my abductor's grip, I prepared to escape.

"At such short notice - it was the best I could find," the Prince shouted, suddenly standing above me.   He grabbed my arm and pulled me further up the steps, out of the surging crowd.   The three men waited for some coins and then, very happily rejoined the rushing flow of humanity.

"I was able to point you out from here," the Prince explained. "Many are dying out there."

Almost intentionally it seemed, four elephants appeared on the scene, compounding the chaos. Their bodies were covered with fabulous painted designs and silver bells hung from their tusks. Across their enormous backs, palanquins rested on pale silk blankets. Trumpeting loudly, they sensed the fear in the swelling crowd. The little Mahouts, sitting behind the flapping ears and large bulging foreheads, only just managed to control their beasts from charging. In one palanquin, the spiritual leader sat beneath the tasseled umbrella, looking impatiently at the crowd around him. With their lumbering gait, and urged forward by the Mahouts, one of the elephants suddenly started sideways at a sudden sound from one of the crashing cymbals. Any other animal would have trampled the people around them, but this elephant instinctively swung its trunk around to push people from beneath its feet. Despite this consideration, several people were pushed to the ground and trampled by the surging crowd - some receiving serious injury. As he surveyed the tide of devastation left behind, a look from the Spiritual leader suggested it was more than a consequence, it was his due! Tersely, he urged his Mahout to make better progress.

The main debate of the Mehla was several weeks away, which gave me a good opportunity to become accustomed to Benares and it's somber odor. The smells from the marsh on the Eastern side of the broad running river, mixed with the earthy incense from the thousand temples. Almost every house seemed to have it's own household deity at its entrance and offerings of food and flowers were regularly made. Despite the omnipresent malnutrition and hunger, I don't ever recall seeing anyone take food from these household temples.

The great Ganga river was a personality in it's own right. Her waters fed the vast plains and, in a sense, provided life to millions. Every morning at sunrise, the entire city made its way to be submerged in those muddy waters. 'Mother Ganga' the Hindus referred to her. People came from great distances on pilgrimage 'to be caressed by the Great Mother'. However the supplicant left the waters, was how their day progressed. So she was always referred to in the most warm terms, like a close relative - as if to gain her favor. Between the buildings, the broad-stepped terraces of the Ghats descended into the river. At times the crowds were so vast that it seemed as though the entire population of India must have been gathered on those steps - yet there was never a lack of people wherever else I traveled. Funeral pyres were almost as common as the dark vultures that circled above. Occasionally people would cover their heads, as one would swoop low and seize the scraps from the dogs in the street.

Even the Jordan River doesn't receive the kind of veneration I witnessed there. Many elderly and sick would walk hundreds of miles, just so that they could be cremated on her banks and their ashes be scattered on her waters. Despite all the bodily functions and refuse being thrown daily into her swift flowing current, for the Hindus, there was no purer place on earth. At the water's edge, men and women of all ages intently murmured their prayers and chants as they carried out their bathing rites. They appeared to directly absorb the vital pranic energy as they looked towards the rising sun. On the steps of one of the world's oldest cities, few people took notice of strangers. There seemed to be a common understanding that we are all God's Chosen.

Many ancient and ornate temples had their foundations undermined by the constant attack of the swift current. Some leaned alarmingly forward above the lapping waters. Few people appeared worried for their safety as they worshipped from second story floors at which, the river now gently lapped. Perhaps it was fatalism, perhaps it was the security of the buildings' antiquity? Ancient trees grew from even older walls at the water's edge. Gypsy women with silver jewelry in their noses, ears and feet - lay washing in the branches of the huge trees. Beside them and oblivious to their shrill laughter, devotees offered gifts towards the rising sun.

Finally came the time of the Kumbha Mehla. We attended many and varied debates in the Great Temple. It was interesting to see the many formalized methods of debate. Some rocked hypnotically backward and forward, occasionally slapping the back of one hand into the palm of the other to emphasis some point. Others used a sing-song cadence to present scriptures by rote. Several were held up by their disciples, while the Guru's assumed some shamanic convulsions. Apparently, the more the Guru wildly threw his head around, was an indication of how close to his God he might be. This hadn't been what I had expected from the Great Debate. The more I heard, the less comfortable I felt. Being only days away from the breaking monsoon and surrounded by thousands of anxious and sweating bodies, I couldn't take any more and had to leave.

The front of the temple was an endless wall of humanity, all eager to hear a single word fall from the lips of their revered Gurus. I found a side entrance and made my way to the rear of the temple enclosure. Climbing through a break in the rear enclosure wall, I found hundreds of people sat in hushed silence on the ground. What stark contrast with the front of the Temple! All eyes rested on an old woman. She sat with her back resting against the retaining wall, dressed completely in white clothing that reminded me of a burial shroud. A white turban lay loosely coiled on her head. Sitting cross-legged, her gaze slowly panned across the seated crowd, making eye contact with each in turn. The merest suggestion of a smile touched the corners of her mouth. For more than an hour, no words were spoken, yet each person she looked to, appeared to be raised to some inner ecstasy. These were the Hari-jans. Poor beyond belief, they came into the cities at night to clear refuse and in return, their community was given a little rice. Being a national festival, they were not openly shunned, as they normally would be. Being of the lowest caste, they weren't even allowed to touch any personal possessions of the high caste Brahmins. They were even lower than the rickshaw boys, whose meager existence at least provided one meal of fish and rice every other day. For this meal the boys sweated and strained, pulling rickshaws they could never hope to own. Yet this strange woman chose to be among these people, rather than in the magnificent Temple. Several among the crowd, modestly made their way to the front and placed rice folded in banana leaves to the side of the old woman. Without taking her gaze from the crowd in front of her, the woman gently nodded her thanks.

An attendant at her side quietly took the offerings and distributed it among the sick and needy of the crowd.

"Who is this teacher," I quietly asked a man at my side.

"She's the Little Mother of Allahabad," he simply stated. He could see that I had never heard of her, so leaned closer in order that his words shouldn't disturb others close by. "They are receiving Darshan from the Little Mother. Each one is recognizing other lifetimes in which the Little Mother also loved and taught them!"

"Does she speak?" I naively asked.

He politely suppressed a smile. "Yes. The Little Mother speaks - but not when she's teaching."

"Why doesn't she attend the Debate?" I asked.

His look suggested a disdain for all debaters. "Little Mother has no desire for recognition. Her service is for love of those that society rejects."

At that moment the woman turned her gaze towards me and flames of love felt to be wrenched from my heart. Her face, instead of being fifty paces away, now seemed only inches from mine and the warmth of her love melted any tension that had accrued during this lifetime.

"She has not taken food or drink for sixteen years. God is her only source of sustenance," I heard the man say.

That night we spent in the home of a merchant, grown wealthy from the shipment of sandalwood. In many ways he reminded me of my Uncle, Joseph of Arimathea. That same sharpness of eye that seemed to be watching just beyond your words. I constantly reminded myself that any prejudice I might feel for my Uncle, I must be careful not to project onto this kind host. Although I didn't necessarily like my Uncle, I always loved him. He was a good man in many respects and always took care of our family. Perhaps it was the familiarity he had with my mother? My brothers and sisters never mentioned any difficulty with his company, yet I... How easily I judged! Perhaps it was mere vanity that drove me to seek this course in life. Why should I, the eldest, seek the spiritual life while my brothers worked in the shipyards of Judaea? I decided at that moment that if I didn't have a clear sign from God, by the time I returned to my homeland, I resolved to take up my responsibilities as eldest son and remain in Judaea!

A servant dressed in flowing silk robes and curled-toed sandals placed a glass of cold sherbet in front of me.

"Then you really are going into politics, Yeshua," the Prince spoke sitting back in a large cushion which was larger than any I had ever seen.

"Why?" I asked confused.

Rather than answer, the Prince deferred to our host.

Raghunath Giri, glanced aside as though not wishing to offend me. He was very like my Uncle, cautious and astute.

"Please," I requested. He looked to the Prince who indicated he should proceed.

"Many believe Little Mother is a fraud," he answered, not wanting to say more.

"Please. I'd like to know everything," I prompted.

"The years, it is claimed she hasn't eaten - can't be verified?" He answered as if that were all that need be said.

"Can't be verified - or can be *proved* to be a lie?"

Our host sat deeper into his cushion, confirmed in his belief that I had taken offense. Perhaps my belief in the woman had shown in my voice. The Prince interceded to save any further embarrassment.

"She's been asked on numerous occasions, to present herself and her story, in front of the debaters at the Mehla - she never has," he quietly spoke, attempting to terminate this line of conversation.

"Why should she!?" I responded, annoyed at my friend's lack of understanding.

"If she has nothing to hide, why shouldn't she?" he answered.

"If God has given a dove wings, should it also present itself - so that it can be proved to be a bird," I answered, making no attempt to concealing my feelings.

"But the debates aren't for the egos of the debaters, Yeshua. They're for all men, so that people can discern between one and another."

I could hardly believe what the Prince was saying. "God's word can't be bought like fruit and vegetables! I saw this woman today and I directly experienced God's love." The word's tumbled out of my mouth and fell heavily. Our host remained silent out of consideration that I was a close friend of the Prince's and he didn't want to offend the Prince. The Prince remained silent.

Immediately I became aware of their discomfort. "I apologize, Giriji. I haven't learned as much as I should for my few years. I meant no offense. I also apologize to you, dear Prince."

Both men generously waved away my apology.

"There's no need," Giri spoke. "Whenever we have Mehlas, the energy level and anxiety always rise." The Prince looked to me, hoping I wouldn't counter this suggestion of anxiety.

"And I'm not used to this heat and humidity," I offered. The Prince was visibly relieved.

"Beside all this religious fervor, the monsoons are overdue and the milk from the cattle isn't good," the businessman inside Giri spoke.

At this time another servant entered the room and waited until she was called forward. Giri gestured her forward. The woman leant close by his ear and spoke low enough for us not to hear.

While she spoke I leaned across towards the Prince and spoke softly. "I *will* speak tomorrow in the temple."

Giri waited for the servant to withdraw before speaking. "There's an old woman who asks to speak with 'the Rabbi from the West'. I presume she means you, Yeshua. She doesn't come to the front entrance - shall I send her away?"

"For any woman to be out at this time of night, let alone one that specifically asks for me - I think I should speak to her."

"I'll come with you, Yeshua. You're in a strange land and strange things happen at the Mehla," the Prince spoke rising from his cushion. Giri put up his hand to forestall the Prince.

"Apparently she'll only speak with 'the Rabbi'. Imagine the cheek!"

The Prince was obviously concerned for my safety, that anyone should want to speak to me alone at this late hour.

"It's safe. I asked a woman for information earlier in the temple and she knew where I was staying. The house of Giriji is well known and respected," I spoke less than truthfully. Giri indicated for the servant to lead the way. Holding a lantern, the servant lead me down many corridors, before crossing an open courtyard. Beneath the darkened rear entrance, a single figure waved towards me. I was right - it was the Little Mother!

Eagerly I crossed the courtyard, dismissing the servant as I went. He was reluctant to leave, but more reluctant to offend a guest of his master's by remaining.

The Little Mother held her two hands together and bowed in greeting.

"Young Rabbi, forgive me for coming at this late hour," she offered.

"I consider it an honor at any hour, more so that it should be now," I spoke from the heart.

"May we walk?" she offered towards the dark lane. "I find words come more easily when this old body is distracted by movement."

"Please," I answered, steadying her arm to walk down the few steps to the lane.

"Today, a strange thing happened," she began.

"What sort of thing?" I inquired, feeling it somehow related to me.

"Normally when I give Darshan, I leave my body and higher energies enter, to do the work that must be done. Today, as I looked at you, I was brought back into the body and told that I must seek you out with information." She paused. "This has never happened before. I don't understand the meaning of it, but nevertheless I bring these words."

As we walked, the Little Mother of Allahabad spoke of many things. She spoke of an ageless Brotherhood who guided man's consciousness. Although she didn't use the name of the Vairagi, as had Guru Tyagi Baba, there was little doubt that these were the same beings by another name.

"Key to everything I've told you, is the number twelve. Everything exists in relationship to everything else. There is a mathematical relationship, hence the true significance of numerology - which I don't begin to understand myself," she modestly added. "I simply bring the words I was given." As she spoke, my thoughts returned to our beloved leader in Qumran. Zaddok often spoke about the Pythagorean school of Mystics. Even in the Gymnasium at Sepphoris, the outer teachings of Pythagoras were revered. The power of numbers was not unknown to me.

"This planet is a Great living Being" the Little Mother continued. "It requires mankind to evolve, so that it too can spiritually progress. With your coming, people will begin to understand the power of three. Your purpose is to take that understanding to the power of twelve - the true key to the spiritual world. Through twelve, the spiritual world is made manifest - mark this well!"

I was confused. Zaddok had spoken about the power within numbers, but had never mentioned that they could be physically embodied in a human being. "Little Mother, I must tell you, your words mean little or less to me!"

"It's not important for the lower self to understand - simply trust! I was told that you should look to the rule, which is divided into twelve inches and three of these form a yard - by which we measure our entire physical world. Be certain - there is no chance here! I was told that the Masters themselves introduced this measurement system, as a reflection of higher truths. It is also why there are twelve months and twelve astrological houses."

"Little Mother, I've heard all you've said with an open heart, but it still means little to me," I pleaded that something of such importance should be so obscure.

"They gave me one more example - should you not understand so far," she spoke, uncertain that her words would mean anything more than she had already said.

"Please. I'm a drowning man and I've seen nothing but a few leaves pass by."

She paused a few moments, knowing that her words would have to be perfectly relayed for any understanding to come about.

"For creation," she slowly began. "It is required that twelve male seed form an exact magnetic relationship - in order that the thirteenth may penetrate the female egg." She looked expectantly to me, waiting for any sign of recognition. There was none, yet her words felt as though they were physically reverberating throughout my body. She recognized something was occurring deep inside me. "Does it mean something?" she finally inquired.

I found myself unable to answer. My throat muscles simply refused to respond. I shook my head in silent denial. The Little Mother smiled sympathetically as if understanding my situation. She repeated the last words of her message, so there should be no mistake.

"For creation, it is required that twelve male seed form an exact magnetic relationship in order that the thirteenth may penetrate the female egg. Remember this Young Rabbi, the masters choose their words well." She nodded as though she had found this out through hard experience. She smiled and was gone into the night. I looked around to thank her, but the dark night simply stared back.

The following day, my glands were swollen and I still found it hard to speak. We arrived early at the Great Temple so that we could be in a good position to witness all the people arriving. The Sadhus were the first. They arrived en mass, at least two hundred. Barely clothed and carrying the strangest items, many resembling instruments of defense. The naked ash-daubed Sadhus entered first, carrying with them an almost tangible silence. Following the naked Sadhus, came the men wearing Arbandhs. These were huge wooden chastity belts that formed a closed circle around the waist and from which hung a simple method of chain and plate, ensuring total sexual abstinence. The intention was to sublimate all sexual energy and transform it into spiritual power and then into eternal bliss. One or two, wore ropes so thick around their waists that they were an enormous burden simply to walk around with. Many of the 'Standing Babas' could barely walk, having open and festering sores. These Babas had made vows to remain standing for at least ten years. They never squat or sit down. Even sleeping, they do while resting against a stick or leaning over a crude rope swing. I later learned that the most severe mortification was Tapasya, the practice of keeping an arm in the air. I recalled my meeting with Ramanath Giri's Guru, his arm so withered. Some Gurus even hold both arms aloft and have *all* their physical needs met by their devotees. The Prince explained to me that if the arm isn't brought down in a specific manner, after all their years of suffering, the Gurus risk death or insanity. One beautiful aspect of this extraordinary mortification is that - unlike in the West - if a Baba is unable to complete his announced time of mortification, he isn't regarded as a failure. In India he is looked on with reverence for having undertaken such a task of willpower at all, since he'll still be regarded as having achieved some unseen spiritual benefits.

While the entrance procession was taking place, I quickly went around the back of the temple to see if the Little Mother had come. She hadn't and there was no sign of her followers. Surprisingly, I wasn't disappointed. It was as if the message she had delivered was all I needed from her.

The Prince, guessing where I had been, smiled inquiringly when I returned. I shook my head.

"It couldn't have been meant," I vaguely spoke.

As the main procession with its more grand arrivals entered the Temple, we allowed ourselves to be swept along with the eager human tide. As vast as the inner temple was, there was barely enough room to turn around, without striking another person. Many individual concentrations of people had formed, each with a central speaker. Some spoke quietly out of consideration for others. Some spoke more loudly, so that they might be more easily recognized. One of the loudest, I recognized as being the owner of the elephant that had terrified so many people. He wore a simple Dhoti suit. Even though a foreigner, I could see his quality of cloth was far beyond those that surrounded me. I listened for some time as he spoke of the caste system and it's initiation by spiritual Masters since the dawn of time. The basic nature of his talk was reasonable enough but the underlying thrust of his argument wasn't. He suggested that man should accept his lot, since this was divinely ordered. At this, I felt anger rising inside myself and decided I should remove myself immediately from this man's influence.

Leaving the Prince behind, I pressed further into the vast crowd. To one side of the temple, a beautiful and intricately carved marble stairway rose fifteen feet above the heads of the crowd, to a speaker's podium. Almost overpowered by the heavy bodily odors and burning incense, I managed to push forward and get close enough to the steps to hear the words of the speaker now sat at the top. The man, or rather boy, was speaking of the reverence we should be paying to the ground beneath our feet. He appeared little more than twelve years of age and had a shock of unkempt red hair. The pale marble held more color than his cheeks did. His eyes were entirely black, without any white surround. Although only young, he had a presence and charisma I had rarely seen before and completely captivated the audience. His gaze seemed to address each and everyone in front of him.

"We live in the most interesting time history has ever known - and Mother Earth cries out, as though giving birth to the most hideous beast," he spoke, hardly raising his voice.

"Who is responsible?" he asked, expecting a direct answer from someone in the audience. Some called out 'Mankind', others 'Greed'. The crowd waited, expecting him to point a finger at some specific member of the audience. He continued, unprepared to address his own rhetorical question.

"The earth gives us life! We are the dust that has risen to believe it is its own creator! It is the finger of God that touched this dust. That impression still remains - in our hearts," he spoke punctuating his words with an inordinate pause.

"We have to learn to adjust our heart beat to that of Mother Earth," he continued.

One man, apparently a spiritual teacher and surrounded by his own devotees, called out.

"Kumarji, you say we should love Mother Earth, but if we don't love our neighbor - how can we begin to love a huge abstract like the Earth," his question barbed, he smiled towards his supportive devotees.

"Your question is already answered," the boy softly spoke. "The smallest of kindness to your neighbor, is a kindness to the planet - there is no separation."

"We honor our Gods, why should we show kindness to those that don't even recognize our faith?" the man retorted.

"All Gods are one," Kumar spoke without any animosity.

A commotion began at the side of the steps and an old man called out.

"You're a liar, who calls himself Kumar," the old man shouted as others tried to physically restrain him. Again he shouted, but I couldn't hear his words, because others tried to shout him down.

Kumar turned his gaze towards the man. "Your time has come old man, go in peace." The old man gripped his chest and staggered forward into the arms of another. The old man's eyes closed in pain. He slipped quietly to the floor. Angry questioning voices were raised and some men began to climb the stairs, suggesting that Kumar was responsible for the man's death. A large bearded man managed to get ahead of the angry assailants and held up his arms as he addressed the increasingly angry crowd.

"Let Kumar speak," he glowered at any that tried to pass him.

The spiritual teacher who had earlier heckled the boy, now gained control over his assembled devotees and made a show of mediating.

"Yes. Let Kumar speak! Let him tell us how his God has allowed him to strike down this poor fellow." The man smiled as a lion might, after eating its fill of some prey and allowing the carrion to pick at the remains.

Kumar surveyed the crowd as though looking across a ripening field of crops. He spoke almost unconcerned for his immediate safety.

"This man has been angry for many years, over the loss of a goat to a neighbor's dog. The truth is, he had been told many times to tie up the animal and yet, he let it stray into the compound where this dog was chained. The dog was used to protect and warn the villagers of any tigers that came at night. He had a responsibility to the goat!"

"Yet, your words killed him!" the teacher called out.

"No," Kumar calmly answered. "The anger had eaten his heart - and he had made a vow to his God. He was to have died two years ago. Instead, he made a promise that he would dedicate his life to the service of Shiva, until he could hear truth spoken at the Kumbha Mehla."

"- And you claim to speak that truth?" the man asked belligerently.

68

"You only have to look around to see that there must at least be a seed of truth, among so many 'enlightened' speakers. I simply knew of the bargain he had made - and wished him well on his Great Journey."

The young boy lightly descended the stairs as he spoke. His detractors backed away, in fear that he might also speak directly to them. Before walking away, he spoke, almost as an afterthought. "Remember this well - there is here today, a true son of God. He will take a golden sword and cut the suckling child from his mother's breast. There will be unspeakable pain, but the child will learn that only the love of God can sustain the true man. He will teach by example and his footprints will remain for two thousand years."

Many heads turned to each of the speakers in turn, as if there would be some heavenly sign - I saw none.

As the body of the dead man passed us, I overheard a couple of men talking about the incident.

"It's true, he was an angry man," the first said.

"Yes, but that boy was lying," the other replied.

"Of course he was, it couldn't possibly have been Kumar."

I couldn't restrain my curiosity any longer, so I assisted in carrying the man through the crowd. By this simple action I recognized how changed I was from the boy that had left Judaea. Merely by being in close proximity to a dead body before, I would have had to undertake many days purification. In India it was as if I had thrown off my cultural conditioning and recognized few limitations within the fields of Belief and Spirituality.

"Excuse me," I began. "I'm a stranger to this festival. Why do you say this boy Kumar lies?"

"Because it's a joke," one answered while the other nodded in agreement. "My Uncle saw the real Kumar at the Kumbha Mehla in Srinagar."

"So why is that impossible?" I asked.

Both men looked at me as though I was an ignorant peasant. "Because that was forty eight years ago and he was a child then!"

The two men pushed through the crowd with the help of others who knew the deceased.

69

After listening to several more speakers in different parts of the temple, I again found myself back on the periphery of the 'elephant' Guru. He was still talking about the Caste system.

"What about the lowest caste - the Hari-jans?" someone asked.

"Their purpose is to serve those who are on the spiritual path," the Guru answered.

"Who is *not* on a spiritual path?" I asked, unable to restrain myself.

"Ah a stranger among us! Perhaps you would be kind enough to share a few words?" he spoke patronizingly.

"I am indeed a stranger among you. I'm curious - you suggest there are those among us who are not on a spiritual path?" I repeated.

The Guru cautiously stepped back. "You know our caste system?"

"I've learned something of it. It's said that there is a hierarchical structure into which we are born and, as we gain credit in each life, we progress higher," I answered.

The man applauded and encouraged others to follow suite.

"Indeed you have learned something of our ways," he spoke turning away, addressing his audience rather than me.

"You haven't answered my question sir," I prompted.

"Because you don't truly understand the question, Sir," he answered dismissively, barely looking towards me.

"That's why I attend the Mehla, hoping to find wise men who might 'educate' me," I responded. "Am I a lost cause - are there no wise men present?"

The devotees stiffened that anyone should reply in such a familiar manner to their revered Guru. Sensing a response was needed, the Guru smiled before speaking.

"You ask, who is not on a spiritual path?" he questioned. I smiled and nodded as amiably as I could under the circumstance.

"The Brahmin is the highest caste and for him, the Holy scriptures of India were written, ten thousand years ago. The lower castes gain credit by knowing their place in the structure and nature of Spirit." He chose his words carefully, aware that any slip wouldn't go unnoticed by the crowd.

"And how are they to know 'their place'?" I inquired.

"Because we will tell them," he quietly answered.

"'Tell them' - not 'teach them'?" I queried.

"You're being argumentative Sir. You don't seek either truth or education!"

"No, you're mistaken Sir. I merely wish to know how this great teaching reaches the people? - The same people who starve at your palace gates and envy your dogs!" I now spoke angrily.

I felt many eyes on me and could see members of the Guru's following, grouping to take action. Rather than wait for them to take the initiative, I spoke first.

"Come! Let us go to the gates of this august Temple and invite the 'Untouchables'. Why would God want them to be the last to hear his words. Being the lowest, they should fully understand your importance. Come, I'll bring them." I turned to leave. Almost as a parting of the sea, a pathway opened up. Whether it was because these people feared my words or they didn't want to be contaminated by the recognized 'ungodly', I don't know; but It was certain, I wouldn't be ignored. I looked around for the Prince as I made my way towards the main exit, but he was lost in the sea of heads.

As I emerged from the temple, a scuffle was breaking out near the outer gate. Several of the 'Untouchables' had tried to enter the debate and were being very forcibly ejected. Unable to reach the gate because of heaving mass of people, I climbed up the low perimeter wall and moved to where the ejected Hari-jans were being cared for by their friends. They apparently expected more abuse from me and edged further from the wall. Blood ran down from the ear of one of the men, while two women tended him.

"What was your crime?" I called out. Several men uncertainly formed a barrier in front of the ejected men, fearing I might be trying to identify the guilty party for further punishment.

"I'm a stranger here and I have no power over you," I tried to placate their fears. "Please tell me, what offense caused you to be beaten like this?"

"You were inside, you know," one answered distrustfully.

"I don't know your customs - please explain," I pleaded.

71

"These men risked death by attempting to listen," the first man explained.

"But why?"

"We are told, they would defile the Debate.   We are Harijan?" he spoke fatalistically.

"Which one of you was not born of a woman?" I demanded.

They looked perplexed, but were prepared to listen.

"None, Sahib," one suspiciously answered.

"And God saw fit to place the seed of creation in your mother's womb.   Would God see one fruit more worthy than another, or would each be a different reflection of the original source?" I challenged the apparent leader.

He understood my point but knew these were dangerous words, so answered carefully.

"But each fruit serves a different purpose, Sahib."

"Are the feet any less a part of God-created man than the hands?   A mirror is worthless without a reflection, no matter how fleeting or disconnected that image might be.   Climb this wall and hear the Holy words for yourself - then you can choose your place in society.   Truth is realized inwardly, not spoken third hand by men who claim authority through accident of birth."

I felt a sharp stabbing pain and turned to find at least fifty men surrounding me.   One had thrust a small sharp trident into my lower back.   Several carried awesome ceremonial cudgels and were ready to test their efficacy.

"What is it you want?" I asked recognizing several of the speakers from the debate.   The trident hadn't pierced too deep and I was able to stem the bleeding by pressing my hand firmly against the small of my back.

The 'elephant' Guru stepped forward in recognized authority.

"You are not welcome here, young Rabbi," he calmly spoke.

"Has God spoken?" I questioned provocatively.   "Since this festival is to bring us closer to him, I presume only he would have the authority to make such a judgment."

"Those you see here," he gestured to his armed supporters, "represent his voice.   And it is their judgment that you should not only leave the festival, but also return to your own land."

Although I didn't turn around, I sensed the Hari-jans were crowding close against the low wall behind. I looked into the cold eyes of the Guru and saw no spark of compassion.

"Man was made in the image of God's spirit," I began. "When man honors any man, he honors God. What he does in thought word or deed - he also does to God."

"The temple is the place for debate, Rabbi," the Guru spoke trying to silence me. Out of the corner of my eye I could see many Hari-jan entering by the main entrance, determined not to be stopped.

"When you caste away the Hari-jan 'Untouchables', you also reject God," I spoke clearly so that all should hear. There was an audible intake of breath as the crowd looked to the Guru for some corrective reaction.

"Now you insult India's learned men," he retorted, indicating that I should be seized!

"But I see none before me," I answered as one of the Guru's assistants swung a serrated mace towards my head. Immediately, the mace was caught in a trident, thrust forward from the Hari-jan behind me. The combined force of the mace and the trident knocked me sideways to the ground. Immediately I jumped up and held up my arms, otherwise it was certain a very bloody fight would ensue.

"This is no place for bloodshed!" I called out.

"You have fine words, Rabbi, yet you dare question our authority in these matters." The Guru urged his men forward, having little fear of the Hari-jans. He hadn't seen the tide of Hari-jans that had closed behind his own group.

"Your God - Brahm - does he exalt one man over another?" I asked. "Or is this Man's interpretation of his word? What arrogance sets one man higher than another when we've all entered the world, naked and wet from our mothers." Now, hundreds had left the great Temple, hearing about the trouble on its doorstep.

Another Guru stepped forward from the threatening crowd.

"Rabbi, you defile this sacred gathering by talking of such things! You should leave now!"

I could barely believe my ears, that this ignorance should find support at such a gathering.

"You talk of lofty matters here, yet keep the 'Untouchables' from your door. I've heard many fine speeches here that talk of love, but not one word of inviting these 'unworthies' to sit at your learned tables. Can't we spare a few spiritual crumbs? Come, I invite them myself!" As I stepped forward, thirty or forty Hari-jans jumped the wall. Suddenly the Guru's men realized just how many Untouchables were around them and held their weapons in readiness. Seeing a wall of weapons in front of me, I turned to the Hari-jans, now swarming over the low wall.

"If you are told that God's kingdom is in the sky, then be sure the birds will be with God before you. If you are told God's kingdom is in the sea, then the fish will be first!" Turning back to the Brahmins, I could see they were incensed by my words. I continued as I walked along their line. "Instead, I tell you, the kingdom of heaven is inside you - look no further! When you come to truly know yourself, then you will become known. Those that have been decreed as 'Untouchable', listen to me. You should enter the Temple now and hear truth spoken - before it is manipulated by such men!"

One of the Swami's among the Brahmins called out above their heads. "Rabbi, why do you seek such certain death - is life so meaningless to you?"

"Death is my friend, but I don't seek it," I called back.

Then, I saw the Prince push his way to the front of the Brahmins.

"Fellow Brahmins, let me speak! Hold your weapons," he shouted as he raised both arms to show he wasn't carrying any weapons. Both factions stepped fractionally back so that he could be heard.

"This young Rabbi speaks truth and is a man of God. I brought him to our lands as an honored guest, recognized by the Llamas of Tibet," he wrung his hands together pleading for their consideration.

"He has desecrated our Temple and now preaches to the Hari-jans! He mocks the caste system of our fathers!"

"He deserves punishment before God," another called out.

"For the mistake of bringing a stranger so young to our sacred gathering, I beg your forgiveness. If he speaks truth then there is no blame. If his words are false, his words will fall on hearts of stone - why fear him?"

"We don't fear him, but he has reviled the name of Parabrahm and the Law is clear - he should die," the 'elephant' Guru softly but crisply spoke.

"Then show this stranger that Brahm is a God of mercy; let him leave with his life and in a state of ignorance. Many of you know me - I am Prince Ravanna and I beg you to listen?"

A beggar with no legs called out from the entrance gate. "Are you from Orissa?"

"A man there knows me," the Prince answered, pointing towards the legless man.

Voices among the Hari-jans spoke up.

"It's the Prince who opens his kitchens to the poor!"

"No Brahmin would defile his own kitchens in such a way," another called out.

"I am the Prince of Orissa and I am a Brahmin!" the Prince called out.

Quickly discussing among themselves, the Hari-jans started to lower their weapons. I walked over and kissed the Prince on his cheek in gratitude, but could not deflect my anger.

"Thank you sweet Prince, but I must speak. I ask all you learned Swamis and Gurus of the Ganges, do the Vedas not say that no man can right a wrong, except he who does the wrong?" I looked to the Gurus but none dare answer me.

"You say I have defiled your Temple? By killing me - do you want to take up the load of *my* Karma? How can you know what you ask!" I directed my question towards the 'elephant' Guru so that someone should be forced to answer.

"A man who isn't wise enough to accept the council of his friend the Prince - and yet presumes to lecture us on the ancient texts, should either be condemned to madness by Krishna, or to death by us," he answered, angry at the Prince's intercession.

The Brahmins now had reinforced their numbers from the Temple and greatly outnumbered the Hari-jans. The Hari-jans could also see the maneuvers and formed a closer grouping at my back.

"Don't act for me," I turned to address the Hari-jans. "Or you will take on the Karma of blood. I'm sure our 'learned' friends will kindly point out however that no spiritual strength is gained in idleness of spirit - but don't act now. Know that as the lowest of the castes, you stand to gain the most - if you recognize the Temple is in your own hearts - not at the feet of these men!"

"If what you say is true, Rabbi, where should we find the money to pay for sacrifices to honor our Gods?" a Hari-jan called out from the rear.

The Brahmin's smiled, knowing these men had no means of earning any money and what little food they could get, would never be 'wasted' in sacrifice.

"You see how they smile?" I pointed out. "That which you've been told to burn in sacrifice at their shrines - is thrown away! No blessing attends anyone who takes food from hungry mouths and destroys it by fire!"

Incensed at this attack on their power base, the Brahmins surged forward to seize me, but the Hari-jans moved faster and formed a protective ring around me. Perhaps unwisely, I pushed through my protectors to confront the Brahmins.

"Make human hearts your shrines and fan the flames of Love!"

"Rabbi, you speak with such authority and confidence, for one so young. Who is this God and where are his priests?" a Brahmin mockingly asked.

"The God I'm coming to know, is everywhere. He can't be enclosed by walls. When men become afraid of God, they begin to dress up in fancy clothing and call themselves priests or Gurus. Many claim they have the authority to restrain God's anger with prayers. When they fail to win favors by prayer, they buy him off with sacrifice of a living creature. I tell you, the little money you do posses, should be spent on food for your children, not on letting the blood of innocent creatures."

At this, one of the Swamis produced a sharp chained-flail which he flicked towards my eyes. I brought up my left arm and catching the stinging weapon, pulled the man forward to the ground. Barely before I could look up, a sharpened wooden stake struck the man in his left shoulder. The tide could no longer be held back and hundreds began fighting, with deadly intent. This was not civilized warfare. Men fell around me, crudely struck with blunt and jagged instruments. I stood amid the bloody carnage in disbelief. Only minutes earlier, these same men were preaching the sanctity of life and what it is to be in harmony with God's will. Now all I saw was blind hatred. This was where structured religion had brought us! Suddenly, I was seized and wrestled to the ground. A sheet was thrown over my head and a cloth put in my mouth. As I struggled, a rope was tied around my hands and legs. Several men fought off my would-be abductors, but without success. I felt the weight of one of my assailants fall on my body as he was struck dead and his warm blood soaked through the cloth to my face.

"We have him," I heard one shout out as he helped drag my body across the hard ground. All around, the sounds of the dying grew dimmer, as I felt myself being placed on my back on some moving horse-drawn cart. Shortly after, I felt bundles of wood and an assortment of large baskets piled above me. The accumulated weight pressed my head painfully against the rough boards, making breathing difficult. The cart had recently been used to transport cattle dung and the coarse smell still lingered.

From the receding sound, I estimated we must be heading for the city limits. Then I heard many urgent feet running after the cart.

"Hold there!" I heard a voice order.

"Why? I'm traveling to Jaunpur. Is there a problem?" I heard the cart-driver ask with concern.

"What do you have on that cart - and don't waste my time!" the man curtly ordered.

"All I have is what you see - herbs, baskets, some cloth and firewood."

"Then you won't mind us searching, will you," the voice shot back.

I heard the shaft of a spear crisply penetrate the branches.

"Careful with that," the man objected. "I don't want holes in my new cloth."

I could hear a deliberate pause as the searcher rounded the cart, closer to where I lay.

"Just one hole won't be too difficult to repair," I heard his words as a sudden sharp pain cut into my side. The weight above me was too heavy to even flinch and the gag in my mouth had drawn any moisture from my mouth.

I wasn't aware I had passed out, until the fresh air hit my face. We were at least an hour outside of Benares. The gag was taken from my mouth. One man supported me beneath the shoulders while the second tried to guide water into my mouth. I was still unable to swallow because of the dryness and most of the water spilled down onto my chest.

"Rabbi, are you all right?" the one I later learned to be Krishna asked. It seemed such a stupid question that all I could raise was a nodding smile.

"He's barely conscious," the voice I recognized as the driver spoke.

"How could you carry him like that?" Krishna harshly asked.

"Would you prefer I brought a corpse!" the driver answered in kind, not prepared to accept any responsibility.

"But look! He's got a wound in his side and blood all down the side of his face. Give me some cloth to clean him," Krishna spoke, looking closely into my eyes. "I don't think the blood on the head is his - we can thank God for that at least. The wound in his side doesn't look too deep either."

"Yes, but it's many days to Ladhak," the driver answered.

The blood from my head was soon cleared away and my side bandaged.

"The Prince asked us to watch you," Krishna volunteered. From my look he could see I wondered why.

"The Prince's own words were that he wanted us to watch you for 'reasons of safety'. He felt that the Mehla was a Tiger trap, but he didn't know if you were the goat or the Tiger," he laughed. "I think you're a little of both. That's why I ordered Ali to take you by force - to save any possibility of mistake."

"Where is the Prince?" I managed to speak in a rasping whisper.

Krishna looked less than hopeful towards Ali the driver.

"I saw him go down beneath several Hari-jans. Those that hadn't heard him speak, mistook him for the other Brahmins," Ali answered.

"He's dead?" I questioned, my voice gradually returning to normal.

Ali looked away and nodded his head.

"Many died today," Krishna tried to console.

My heart ached with the knowledge that it had been my direct actions that had been responsible for so much bloodshed.

Twice, armed horsemen surrounded us and inquired if we had seen a Rabbi and the Prince of Orissa. Fortunately, we had seen them approaching and I had hidden in the sparse scrub without being seen. A large reward had been posted for my body. The positive news was that they were also searching for the Prince - which suggested he might still be alive! As we approached the foothills of the Himalayas, the oppressive humidity of the plains began to subside. I had no idea that a country could be so beautiful. Judaea had it's jeweled oasis and the greenery of Galilee, but nothing like the lush dark vegetation that surrounded me now.

Krishna had grown up with the Prince and was able to tell me a lot about him. The Prince was dearly loved by many people. At the age of seven, he had begged his own father to let him live with the Yogis for two years. He had never mentioned this to me. Although he could have remained in the palace of Orissa, living a life of total indulgence - he chose the extreme rigors of the Yogic discipline.

"Ladhak is cut off from the rest of the world - at least, for nine months of each year. The air is crisp and sweeter than any you've tasted before," Krishna spoke savoring the memory and looking forward to our arrival.

"The mountains?" I asked.

"There are a few routes in, but because of the altitude, the snow remains," he answered. "You'll like Ladhak."

We crossed many raging rivers and the stone bridges gradually gave way to rope and wood. The cart had been left behind many days earlier and with it had gone Ali, leaving Krishna and myself to continue alone on foot. The steep paths along the mountain passes were too rough for any animal except the short-legged Tibetan horses and large, cow-like animals I learned to be Yaks. Some paths we traveled, were simply loose shale, where one false step would have sent us falling several hundred feet to the churning waters below. Most of the way we traveled, appeared to be little used. Several of the mountain ravines could only be crossed by a three-rope bridge, which consisted of one rope no thicker than my arm, on which we walked and two either side, over which we rested our arms. Fortunately the mountain peaks protected us from the most severe winds, since these would have without doubt caused the bridges to sway and us to fall.

My knowledge of herbs, learned from Udraka, soon healed the wound in my side and gave us the needed energy for such a grueling journey.

"The Monastery of Hemis," Krishna broadly announced after several weeks of strenuous exertion.

From a distance it would be hard to detect the Monastery was there at all. The grey stone buildings set back into the grey hillside. The stone had been set irregularly, though with perfect precision. What had caught my eye first, was the brightly colored prayer flags that danced and jumped in the gusting breeze.

As we approached, the long Tibetan horns trumpeted loud and shrill. Some form of ceremony appeared to be in progress and saffron-robed monks lined the tall rising steps to the Potalla. There was only one road to the Monastery, so we could hardly avoid being involved in whatever ceremony was being undertaken. As we neared the base of the steps, a shrill discordant assembly of musical instruments joined the regular trumpeting of the horns. An aged monk wearing bright yellow robes stepped forward to greet us.

"The Llamas of Hemis have long awaited your return Master," the old monk spoke bowing low before us and then placing prayer shawls around both Krishna and my necks. I looked confused to Krishna, since I had no idea he was well known to this area - let alone be addressed as 'Master'. Krishna seemed equally confused.

"We have heard of the dangers that pursued you since last we met," the monk continued. I stepped slightly aside so that they might greet each other less formally.

"I forget your sense of humor Master. We have looked forward to this moment for a long time," he directly addressed me.

"I think you must be mistaken good Abbot," I cautiously ventured as I looked around.

"Forgive me - it's been a long journey," he apologized.

"No, I mean - I don't recall meeting...." He paused for a moment and then smiled. "It was many years ago, in Judaea. You were a boy of two or three. I am Lun. I came with the Abbots, Hor and Mer?"

Now I recognized the familiarity. The three Tibetans who had visited our family in Nazareth and given us warning about Herod Antipas!

"Lun?" I repeated in disbelief.

He smiled in acknowledgment. "The years have not been kind to me - we have been apart so long, and longer."

"Longer?" I queried.

"You have no recall?" he answered, disappointed.

"Only of your visit."

"Then come with me and see the monastery. The air and the stones will soon bring back the many years you spent here teaching the younger brothers," he spoke with a certain sadness.

I looked to Krishna, to see if he could throw any light on the matter, but he looked equally mystified.

"But Abbot Lun, no one passed us on the way... No one knew we were coming, how did you?" Krishna asked, voicing my own thoughts. The old Abbot smiled patiently, before determining we really didn't know.

"There are better ways of communicating than on foot," he simply stated without further explanation. He lead us slowly up the steep steps, where it was clear we had been expected for some time. Several of the elder monks smiled in a familiar way, looking for recognition or acknowledgment. Lun raised his hand indicating they shouldn't expect more at this time.

"Are the Abbots Hor and Mer also here?" I asked.

"Soon," he answered. "Messages were sent to Ephesus immediately it was known the 'Llama in Waiting' was to return."

We were taken to a room high in the Potalla, where food and drink were provided.

"I thought that, after your long journey, you would like a little rest and privacy," Lun simply stated. "The room for Krishna is across the corridor. One of our monks will remain outside the door - if there should be anything you require." With that, he bowed low and left us alone. It was true, we were both exhausted, probably from the altitude. Neither of us touched the food, but went straight to bed.

My open window faced out across the valley. The light had faded and only a pale outline of the snow-capped peaks remained visible. A resonant chanting from the monks continued long into the night and lulled me into a deep sleep. Suddenly, a bright light appeared in the room. I opened my eyes, thinking it must be Krishna coming in to talk, but there was no one. Even the light wasn't visible. I looked around for the source of the disturbance, but there was nothing. The chanting still continued, but sounded to come from a far greater distance. I lay back and closed my eyes again. Again the golden light appeared in my head. From the central source of this profound light, the shape of countless figures appeared. Three stepped forward and took on specific form and features. Although young of feature, they emanated an ageless wisdom.

"Yeshua," the leading figure communicated without speaking.

"It is I, Lord," I answered from my heart.

"Yeshua, the time has come for the veil of past lives to be raised." Immediately these words were spoken, an array of picture cards appeared before my eyes. The moment my eyes set on one of the cards, a procession of images and emotions passed through me and I knew them to be true. This present life was less than a single atom in my greater body, yet every other single atom had grown so that this life should be the fulfillment of all the others. My entire being lay finely balance on the edge of the sharpest damask knife, a breath either way could prove disastrous. Events, even down to the smallest detail were shown to me, so that I knew that even a pebble displaced beneath my feet, had meaning and consequence. No energy was expended on my account, yet I felt as if my atoms were incapable of holding one more single thought or movement - without my physical body being consumed by ethereal fire.

"You are correct Yeshua," the voice answered, as if I had voiced the thought. "You have spiritually traveled further than any man born of flesh. Without our help, you have perfected the human body and stand on the threshold of making Spirit manifest in this lower world." His words carried vibration pregnant with far deeper meaning, suggesting a transformation beyond the world of the senses.

"Your steps will reverberate for two thousand years, when another of our line will take up the mantle. Know that we are always with you, yet you sit at the head of the table. Your destiny lies in Egypt and the entire Universe will hold it's breath as it awaits the outcome." With those words, the figures were gone, while I remained bathed in the brilliant and Divine Golden light. The slightest movement of my lower self, wondered at the words. My true self knew the words and their meaning.

The following day I woke feeling as if my flesh had been burnt. Any slight movement caused a stinging sensation in the muscles. My skin threatened to tear if I made any sudden motion. It was as if the true self was too fine for the gross body in which I now moved. Suddenly I remembered - this was my twenty fifth birthday! I wondered if any man had received such a wonderful present as I had had that previous night.

"I slept a sleep I haven't known since I was a baby," Krishna beamed as we were being lead towards the main Temple.

"How do you mean?" I asked, wishing to divert the conversation away from my own sleep pattern.

"It was dreamless. I floated in a warm soft cloud. I feel regenerated. Normally at this altitude, my body aches like a sixty year old's."

"I trust the Llama in Waiting slept well?" Lun inquired as we approached the steps of the main Temple.

"Like no other," I answered smiling and wondering if the Abbot knew more than I told. We offered incense towards the huge and garlanded stone Buddha. Curiously, the Tibetan mannerisms were as familiar to me as my own Judaic upbringing. Lun looked surprised that I knew the finger mudras and spoke a now familiar Sanskrit chant. He waited until I was done.

"You seem changed from yesterday, Yeshua?" he queried.

"It was a sleep from which few men would wish to wake," I quietly spoke out of Krishna's hearing. Lun nodded his head in understanding.

"What I was unable to speak yesterday, I can now tell," I spoke openly. "My path doesn't lead to Lhasa." Lun looked disappointed, as did the other Llamas close by. "With me, it has been decided that tradition will have to wait. It's better that I remain unknown. That's why I have chosen this Monastery of Hemis."

Now it was Krishna's turn to look confused. He had no idea I knew about this destination prior to our meeting and, until the previous night, nor did I. "One day I might explain," I spoke to recognize his confusion. The previous day I wouldn't have had the understanding - or the wisdom!

The next few weeks were spent in rest. Mostly, I just walked and talked with Abbot Lun. The library was my greatest joy. The thin parchments pressed between wooden blocks answered mysteries for which nations had gone to war. Many of the wonders I'd seen in India were explained by simple physics, others were more wonderful than I had understood. Throughout, the quality that differentiated the wonders of Man from the wonders of God, was Love. In it's basic simplicity I had always understood that. Now I knew it to be a tangible force or energy field that underlay all matter. It wasn't merely a feeling of benevolence; it was a cognitive and tangible force that existed purely through God's will. By its conscious use, man sat at the right hand of the Creator.

"What has been the hardest burden for you to bear, Yeshua?" Lun asked me in that forthright manner that from any other man, would seem offensive. I thought for a moment.

"The poor," I answered. "Especially in India. They begin work before first light and finish well after dark. Their only hope - beyond the next bowl of rice, is to lie down on their final day among Lord Buddha's city of the dead."

"But it has always been this way," Krishna objected.

"History is a poor judge of what is right, Krishna. The history we have been given is the greatest political lie. Histories are written by the victors. The stones are laid off center. One day this building will fall and each man will look to another and know the only truth, is that which lies deep in our hearts." It was clear Krishna didn't understand my words and that any more, would only confuse him still further.

"And past lives?" Lun asked, recognizing my dilemma.

"Brief glimpses. We have forgotten where we came from. If people stilled the mind for even a moment, they would recognize that Heaven is only a breath away. It's a state of mind, not something for which one must endlessly suffer, in order to achieve after death."

"What about Hell, if we don't follow 'right action'?" Krishna cautiously asked.

"Again, a state of mind created my Man."

"But what about India's great Holy men? I understand you met and learned from many?" Lun asked - more for Krishna's benefit.

"A Paradox - those that claim to be such, only succeed in pushing that heavenly state further from them. At the Mehla I saw many dress up in bright clothing and strut like peacocks. Spirit must turn away in disgust at such show. As the sacred scriptures tell, a day will come when every man will be a priest and not have to display himself in special clothing to advertise his piety." I spoke with a growing anger, recalling the abuse of spiritual teaching. Recognizing this in myself, I became silent.

"Will we see that day?" Lun spoke softly.

"Dear Master Lun, I wish I could say. The only future we have the right to know, is our own. For myself, I have been shown glimpses." Lun and Krishna remained silent, quietly forcing me to say more. Reluctantly I continued. "My purpose is to return to Judaea. The why, I don't know. If we each knew our future, many, myself included, might refuse to go further - so maybe it's a blessing in disguise."

For the next few months, I wandered among the mountains leaving recognized paths and following my intuition. Without fail, a lesson of one sort or another always awaited me. I met extraordinary men, of whom the world has no knowledge. Men who have appeared in historic times - and still live. I was taught that the aging process exists *only* because we believe it exists and that there is no actual necessity to die in the way we understand it. Essentially : to live in the moment, we can live outside of time and therefore not subject to the ravages of time. These men rarely appear in the outside world, but are directly active in guiding the consciousness of world leaders. The world leaders largely have no idea of their influence and simply look upon their own insights as being 'inspired'.

One elderly Yogi I stayed with, taught me a considerable amount about manipulation of the elements. To this day I still don't know his name - he never offered it and I never asked. Perhaps it was an effect of the extreme altitude, but by this time my thoughts held a profound clarity. We both understood that for the Self-realized man, coincidence doesn't exist. The Yogi and I had crossed paths and both knew it was for the purpose of my education. He sat at the entrance of a small cave, in full lotus position, freely suspended - three feet above the ground. This was the first time I had seen genuine levitation.

"How do you do that?" I asked.

"How is it that you can't?" he replied.

"It's against the Laws of Nature," I replied.

"Is that your belief or your knowledge," he asked with an infectious grin, still floating in the air.

"Both - I think," I answered hesitantly.

"Wrong," he answered carelessly.

I thought carefully before speaking again. He waited patiently for my next question. I reached down and picked up some gravel from the ground.

"It is my knowledge," I confidently stated as I pointedly let the stones fall to the ground. He continued to smile and then pointed to a large rock at my side. I watched in disbelief as the rock lifted, seemingly weightless, from the ground and then projected out and down onto the steep mountain slope.

"Your 'knowledge' seems to have limitations," he spoke as if to no one in particular.

"Only God is without limitation," I excused myself.

"Of course," he now spoke directly to me. "That's why you're here."

"You knew I would be coming?" I asked.

"I neither knew, nor did not know," he spoke in as clear explanation as he felt I might understand. "You are here and I have knowledge that you question." He held out his hands to suggest there could be no other way.

He unfolded his legs and, without moving his upper torso was in the perfect standing position as his feet touched the ground beneath him. It was almost as if he had been sitting on some unseen and comfortable chair. I stayed five days in that small yet surprisingly warm cave. Outside, the wind howled mercilessly and on occasion I heard the clear whistling of the Yeti.

"They have been born in the wrong place," the Yogi explained. By 'place' I now understood he meant 'time'. "They are overly sensitive to the human kingdom and the animal, yet belong to neither." Merely being in that Yogi's presence seemed to impart information. His words felt like the superfluous wrappings of truth. Because he maintained a physical body, he seemed obliged to use the vehicle of voice.

"Energy follows thought," he explained levitation. "The next great leap is Faith." From my reaction he recognized this wasn't enough information for my needs. "The air," he gestured around us. "In here, protected by the mountain, you don't feel it on your cheek; but outside, with the wind blowing, you know it exists. It is tangible, it is physical. Since it is physical, you can fix it in space by the energy of thought. Now, knowing it is fixed, have faith and step up onto it." As if to illustrate his point he stepped up several non-existent steps and remained without support in mid-air.

One of the most endearing of this Yogi's qualities was his love for the most childish of jokes. It seemed so strange that a man who had mastered so many of the world's great mysteries should find such amusement in the naive simplicity of childhood.

We never said good-bye. One morning I woke up and the Yogi was gone. I stayed for two more days and nights, but he didn't return. In the coldness of those mountain wastes, I began to wonder if it had all been an illusion, like the mass hypnosis of the Fakirs and their rope tricks. In my heart I knew this was no illusion or hallucination. It was rare but I have had occasion since, to use some of what he taught.

There were many others that either sought me out, or I sought them out. Either way, their knowledge bordered on the super-physical and would most definitely not be condoned by the Brothers of Light, therefore I don't allow my memories to flow that way. Master Lun always commented on how changed I appeared each time I returned to the monastery.

"Its like you bring back the physical characteristics of previous lives," he had said. His words had the effect of crystallizing what I had indeed learned. I did recall each person who taught me now and had taught me in previous lives.

One day as I sat amid the dry and dusty parchments of the Great library, I felt a warmth such as I could recall from the womb - and the deep resonant voice of Master Hor.

"Each step I made closer to the monastery of Hemis, my spirit became lighter. For the past week, no dust has been able to settle on my shoes," he spoke with a beaming smile and low bow. I jumped up and greeted him as though it had only been days since we had been together. The memories were of our lives previously spent in Lhasa.

"Master Lun told me that you have had recall," he explained his familiarity.

"I remember a lifetime of being chased through many dark corridors of the Potalla - by the 'Dark Spirit' of Lhasa," I smiled accusingly.

"But, as I remember, the Dark Spirit of Lhasa often woke with all manner of crawling insects and animals beneath his blankets," he answered with a raised eyebrow. "Did I ever catch you?"

"Once," I answered coyly.

"Remind me."

"You had stayed awake all night...?"

"Now I remember," he laughed. "I placed a tray above the door with several cymbals."

"- And the head Abbot came to ask you a question before retiring for the night!" I continued.

"I think the entire monastery woke up that night - except for one - who found *myself* AND the head Abbot waiting in the dark, when he arrived with three mountain toads," he concluded.

"Certainly one of my most embarrassing lives," I shook my head in pained memory.

"But on a happier note - I've heard that the Prince is alive," he spoke with suppressed excitement.

"- And well?"

"Not so well," he answered, preparing me for bad news. "During the fighting at Benares, he was cut through the collar bone by a scimitar."

"But you said alive?" I reminded.

"Yes, he is alive - and is expected to live. He was carried out with others, who were also thought to be dead. When he was taken to the mass funeral pyre, one of the attendants noticed he was still bleeding, so must still be alive."

"Where is he? I must go to him," I begged, eager that there should be no delay.

Master Hor put his arm around my shoulders in comfort. "That's impossible. You have upset many Gurus and they have thousands of followers - each one eager to avenge the disgrace they believe you've brought on their Gods. As for the Prince, any other, without his strength of Spirit, would have died that same day. The Prince is with an old friend - Udraka." Even as he spoke I felt an immense sense of relief.

"If I hadn't spoken, the Prince would be well today. It's all my responsibility," I spoke, stating the obvious.

"There is no 'responsibility' to be assumed here. Many lifetimes ago, the Prince - through an act of cowardice, caused many people to be executed. This life he had determined that he should face a similar fate - his Karmic debt. That was to have been his final day. Instead he has assisted in bringing the light back to the world," he spoke bowing lightly towards me. "I suspect his feet are now set on the course of Mastership and there is much he can learn from our dear friend Udraka, before releasing the physical body."

How wonderful I thought, to be so certain as Hor appeared to be. For me, my heart ached for those peaceful times in Tibet.

Ahead, lay an uncertain path. It was as if a golden thread spanned across a bottomless chasm and my purpose was to cross that great divide. How easy it would have been just to remain with my old friends and study in that vast repository of man's wisdom!

"There is other news," he spoke more solemnly. "News of your family."

"It's been so many years that 'family' now rings strange to me," I spoke in apology.

"There have been many troubles in your land. Many uprisings have been cruelly suppressed. The city of Sepphoris has known more than it's share. The people who have been thrown off the land have crowded into the city and violent crime is now everywhere."

"It was less than two hours journey from my home," I offered. Hor nodded in considered agreement.

"The Nazarene Essenes have particularly suffered - because they keep their own council."

"But they always served the community, why should they suffer?" I queried.

"Groups of bandits attacked their enclosures," Hor explained.

"For what?"

"The secrets of the Heart that were taught, were believed to be a *physical* treasury."

"They came for money?" I asked in disbelief.

"When one man speaks of *'treasure in Heaven'* and another speaks of *'inner secrets'*, the third man hears 'buried treasure'. The community was burned to the ground - many lost their lives."

"My family?" I asked, fearing the worst.

"Safe," Hor answered. "Although your father passed from this world three years ago - from the Stone Sickness."

"Where are they now?" I asked.

"With someone by the name of Zaddok?" I felt immense relief at hearing my old Master's name.

"Qumran," I explained. "They'll be safe there." Hor remained silent for some moments so that I could feel the weight of his news. Strangely, I felt no loss at the passing of Joseph. Although he was not my biological father, I loved him none the less. Never for a single moment did he ever look on me as anything less than his own son. I observed my own reaction and recognized how far I had traveled. Years earlier, I would have felt the grief at his passing; now I knew he had completed the work he had agreed on before coming into incarnation and for that, I was happy. For the first time in many years I felt the call of Judaea.

"Master Hor," I awkwardly began. "I recognize that no man has the right to the great love I've experienced with my friends now at Hemis. Because of this, I ask one great favor."

Concerned, Hor looked sideways at me. "Ask anything that's within my power and you know it's given."

"Tell me one thing Master Hor, where does my path lead?"

He seemed to almost stagger on his feet before answering. "The Llama in Waiting does me too much credit - to know such a thing. There is nothing I can tell."

"Nothing? One so close to me, must have some Akashic rights?" I spoke, uncertain of my reasoning.

"I have had a dream," he spoke with hesitation. "It has occurred every night since leaving Ephesus."

"Please," I encouraged.

"Voices, in a golden light, spoke of Giza in Egypt."

"Then you have confirmed what I knew to be true," I answered with a heavy heart.

"And that is?"

"Tomorrow, I leave for Judaea."

With great sadness I left Hemis and my beloved friends and set out alone, towards the West. Many nights I shared caves with wild animals and sometimes even berries with the bears. There was never any danger, because I believed there was none. Even when I approached towns and cities, complete strangers invited me into their homes. Only as I approached my own homeland did I begin to see the familiar fear of strangers. Fortunately this was the seventh year of harvest and many fields lay untended, allowing the wild fruits and honey to abound.

As I traveled towards my homeland, I spoke with many people. There was a considerable thirst for truth and I was happy to teach. At first I had spoken with great enthusiasm for the teachings of the Heart and drew great numbers to me. It was not long before I recognized my error. Being swept along by the power of my emotional enthusiasm, many dropped their rational discrimination. While this would immediately bring many numbers to my cause, I recognized it would not sustain them when I was no longer with them. It would be better that passion be left out of my talks, that way the supporting crutch that I provided could not be pulled out from under them once I had left. I recognized too much of the Brahmin Gurus, hidden beneath that cloak of emotional fervor. Each person would have to walk the path on their own, that way they would know the truth of their own spiritual revelation. I would merely point the way.

As the boatman took me across the narrow waters of the Dead Sea, in my heart, I wished the oars to be less swift. Drawing closer to the shore of Judaea, I could see the Essenes laboring in the heat of the mid-day sun. The cattle pulled the wooden plough through the soft soil as a surgeon might use his knife. How hard our forefathers must have worked, to transform this short strip of arid land. This was no less a miracle than the wonderful sweetness of a desert tomato springing from a lifeless and nondescript seed, yet how few could see it.

Had it not been for Antiochus the Maccabee, replacing his own priests for those originally ordained by King Solomon, these devout servants of God would not have been forced to create this miracle of Qumran. The original Temple priests had fled to this part of the desert and kept the Inner teachings intact. How mysterious are the ways of God - by persecuting the original teachings, he had strengthened their resolve. For almost two hundred years, the teachings had passed down in an unbroken line in the Zaddok family.

Qumran had grown since I last saw it. It seemed more enclosed than I remember. More children played at the water's edge, skimming stones across the placid water towards us. One child stood apart from the others, her face transfixed by mine. As I walked up the hill, she walked a few steps behind, without speaking.

"What is your name sweet child," I asked so that she wouldn't be intimidated in speaking to me.

"Rebecca," she answered confidently.

"From which family?" I continued.

"God's," she answered simply. Her answer hadn't been that of a precocious child, but that of a knowing elder. I stopped and looked directly at her in order to determine her understanding. She held her ground and offered no further explanation.

"How easily I forget. Thank you for reminding me, Rebecca. Every man - or child - is my Brother and there is only one true father." I stroked her soft face and we continued up the hill together. How often Spirit uses children. Being closer to the source, there is less interference from the mind I reflected. Again I had made the mistake of judging - even one so young. I hadn't been in the moment. In future I would be more attentive.

At first my mother didn't recognized me and took me for a tradesman.

"At last! Have you brought the cloth?" she asked as she continued preparing the table for dinner.

"Only the cloth that you provided good lady and from it, I hope to have made a man," I joked.

At first she thought I was being insolent and then suddenly realized who I was. She nearly choked with laughter and tears. She could hardly decide whether to sit down from shock or rush forward and embrace me. I quickly collected a seat and brought it to her, so that she could choose either option. She held me so close that I could hardly take in another breath.

"I've come too far to finally have the life squeezed out of me by my own mother," I lightly objected. I had forgotten the warm strength of my outwardly frail mother.

"Yeshu, Yeshu," she simply repeated over and over, the tears streaming down her cheeks.

Word rapidly spread of my return and in moments I was surrounded by a sea of faces. Many I knew and many, I later learned, had come to escape the oppression of the Roman occupiers. Qumran had always been fortunate because of its isolationist policies and self sufficiency. A community, rather than individual tax was paid to the Romans. Beside requiring less administration for the bureaucrats, it meant our group could have fewer dealings with the authorities. We also avoided the political friction that surrounded the bureaucrats.

Both sisters had married in my absence, while my three brothers hadn't. When James arrived home from the shipyard, he avoided coming directly to me, but instead, attended to some apparently important business matters before greeting me. His words spoke of welcome but there was little warmth. After we had eaten, I managed to catch him alone for a few moments.

"You seem less than happy that I returned, James?" I spoke.

"You're mistaken brother," he answered coolly, avoiding my eyes.

"'Brother', spoken like that - wouldn't warm me on a winter's night," I spoke, moving directly into his line of vision.

"Warmth?! You? You've spent this many years among strangers in foreign lands - without a single word to your own family. Not a word about your safety to your own mother. *You* question *me* about 'warmth'?" He could barely contain his anger. What he said was true and there was nothing I could say that would heal his pain.

"What you say is true, James. What would I say - that each day I escaped assassination, through the kindness of friends? Would that have helped? Would my mother have slept a minute longer knowing that thousands could attain untold wealth, simply by displaying my severed head on a wooden pole?"

"And they wanted this without good reason?" he questioned, his eyebrows raised in disbelief.

"Has any man ever died for 'good reason'?"

"None of us could ever better you in debate, Yeshua. Words trip so easily from your tongue. Yet it's us that have had to work in the yards, while you chose to travel the world, keeping the company of strangers rather than the bosom of your own family. And you dare to question me about feeling!" he turned away rather than say more. Never had I felt this darkness strike me so heavily in the stomach. I was speechless.

"And my brothers, they also feel this way," I asked, fearing the worst.

"They're your brothers in name alone, Yeshua!" he spoke angrily turning towards me, so I should feel the full force of his words. "What else would you expect? You're the eldest and haven't married?"

"They wanted to?" I blankly questioned. It was true, I had been beguiled by the East and the years had slipped rapidly by, despite, or rather because of, the many dangers I had faced. In those years, my Brothers and Sisters had grown to adulthood. Being the eldest and unmarried, my brothers weren't allowed by custom to marry.

"You're right James and I have wronged you. I beg your forgiveness," I appealed.

"Deeds can't be erased by a few words, Yeshua. You claim to have studied with so many wise men - yet they appear to have taught you so little," he answered, pleased at my discomfort.

"How can I make amends?" I asked, prepared to make myself totally vulnerable to any request he might make. He thought carefully before replying.

"It's our mother you've wronged most." He paused to see that I didn't object, then continued. "You should agree to do whatever is closest to her heart - *whatever* she asks?"

"Whatever who asks?" my mother spoke from behind. "You seemed so intent over here and I haven't seen my son in nearly twelve years. Come, tell me - whatever *who* asks?" James had seen mother coming but hadn't given any indication.

"I think the Prodigal has something to ask, Mother," James spoke as he came and put an arm around Mary, so that they should both directly face me. I looked in his eyes and didn't recognize my own flesh. How changed he had become, and I to him.

"If there was one gift I could make to you Mother - a gift that only a son whose been absent from those who care most for him could give, what would it be?" I asked, taking care not to let any pressuring by James show in my voice. Mother looked coyly at James, but dare not voice the words. James looked largely away so that it appear that he had no idea what Mother's request might be.

"Please? Anything - you simply have to name it," I encouraged. James' eyes locked onto mine as though the tiger was already pacing, deep inside his trap.

"There is only one thing - but it's too big to ask," mother answered with little hope.

"Speak and let it be done!"

Again she looked to James, who put his hand forward in gesture that I had offered in good faith and that she had the right to speak.

"Beside your safety, there is only one dream I've had since I saw you leave with Prince Ravanna," she cautiously spoke and then stopped.

"Say it," I encouraged.

"That you should be married." Immediately she tried to withdraw her request, recognizing I felt a higher calling.

"It is given," I quietly responded.

Mother put her hands to her mouth, shocked and in fear that she might say something beyond her own control. James watched closely, mistrustful.

"I can't ask that of you," Mother spoke between tears of joy and shock.

"Unless James has taken to being a market entertainer, I believe the words were yours," I joked so that she shouldn't feel the burden of her request. "It's a gift I willingly give. In these dreams, who did you see beside me." She barely dare speak the words, but was finally prompted forward by James.

"Mary of Magdala. An Essene family - a good family living in Cana," she quickly answered before I could change my mind. How little my own mother knew me - that I should give my word and consider changing it! My few years away, had become a lifetime. I put out my arms to encompass both my mother and James.

"Was there ever a more fortunate man? In a single day to gain both a family and a wife," I spoke the words lightly and even James was forced to smile, since this also signaled his own marriage.

"Then I must be about my business - tonight will be a celebration," she held me close against her bosom and then left, barely able to contain her excitement.

"It is a good thing you do in the sight of God, Yeshua," James spoke as if to confirm his own disbelief in my response.

Hardly an hour passed and our courtyard became full of the well-wishers and the purely curious.

James approached with my brothers, Joses, Judas and Simon. My sisters had married and no longer lived in Qumran. The relief of my brothers and their happiness at hearing of their own impending marriages, showed fully in there faces - as did the residue of their distancing from their older brother.   So James *had* spoken for them as well.   It seemed he had also smoothed the waters with them. Their enthusiastic congratulations for my own coming marriage was barely distinguishable from their own anticipation of marriage. Perhaps it was me that had grown distant from them?

"We have come with our Uncle Joseph," Thomas spoke, returning the conversation to more mundane matters.

"Where is he?" I asked looking around the heads of the assembled crowd.

"He wants to speak with you, alone," Simon spoke ominously.

"Then let me go to him, so I can give my thanks for keeping our family safe," I spoke lightly so that the atmosphere shouldn't again turn too serious.   It had been a long day and I craved a little levity.   I recalled my beloved Udraka's words: *'When a wise man hears God's word, he remains silent.   When a fool hears God's word, he laughs at it.   It's in the echo of the fool's laugh that the wise man recognizes truth confirmed'*.   It was because of the importance of events that I made light of it.   One thing I had noticed in my travels, was that those closest to Spirit, had the finest sense of humor.   That's not to say that the funniest men are also the most spiritual!   It was as if God had let them in on the great cosmic joke: that the physical world was truly the word made flesh, but how few could see!   For too long we had stumbled around in darkness, like blind men looking for candles.   The nature of blindness is darkness and the nature of man is Spirit.   This I knew was my journey, to be a revealer of the Light.   Where the path would lead I didn't know - and took comfort from that.

"He waits over there," James spoke, indicating a dark room at the far side of the courtyard.   I made my way through the noisy gathering, briefly greeting those I recognized.   The room was little more than a storage area with a small circular table at which Joseph sat, patiently waiting.

I could have been mistaken, but it seemed he waited for me to greet him, before acknowledging me.   I stepped forward and put my arms out so that we could embrace.

"Uncle, I give thanks that God has looked kindly on us - that you should take such good care of our family."

Joseph stood up and embraced me. There was a reserve in his embrace and a need to speak of matters that might be less happy.

"I don't greet you openly cousin, because there's much we have to discuss - and it's not for the ears of others." His manner spoke of dark deeds and consequence.

"For you to greet me in such manner, after so many years, I fear what you must have to say," I spoke the words lightly but they found their mark. Joseph smiled, at once embarrassed and forthright.

"It's a matter of deep concern - to me and Israel," he answered.

"Tell me, what is in your heart?" I spoke directly, meeting him on the middle ground.

He walked to the door and looked out over the festivities. Without turning back towards me, he spoke. "Yeshua, after you left Judaea, the Romans used their spies to identify all the leaders of the resistance. Many you knew and were old friends. Their blood now feeds the hills of Jerusalem. Many were easy to identify, because they spoke openly - and paid a terrible price."

"And the Nazarenes?" I asked.

"The Essenes haven't spoken to anyone who wasn't an Initiate, so we've survived - so far." He turned to face me, though his head was framed against the light from the door and I couldn't determine his expression.

"You speak as if this has something to do with me," I queried his silence.

"It does."

"How? I've been away so long. I'm the forgotten man of Nazareth," I answered at a loss to his meaning.

"It's *because* you have been away so long," he answered flatly.

"Because?"

"I'll come to that," he dismissed my query with a wave of his hand, as one might dismiss a servant. "With the shipping, I've become somewhat influential with the Romans - they like their luxuries from home. Both of us wish for their earliest return to

Rome. For them, this is the most troublesome region of their *un*Holy Empire."

"Yet they remain?" I pointed out, having as little regard for Roman rule as he did.

"They need Palestine as a buffer against the Parthian Empire. They also need it to protect their breadbasket - Egypt. This land controls the passage to the East - and they have a taste for fine silks and spices."

"Which your ships have cultivated," I interrupted.

Joseph recognized the conflict of interests and slightly winced - as though trade was above moral judgment and was a mere fact of existence. He continued without response. "When the Zealots were massacred, it became clear - at least to a handful of us - that we couldn't overthrow them with mere hit-and-run tactics; something else was needed."

"You were in the resistance?" I asked in disbelief.

"It surprises you?" he asked with a smile. "That's good."

"For how long?" I asked, amazed at this new facet to my Uncle.

"Long before you left Judaea. What better person - a merchant who travels freely between Rome and Judaea?" he spoke reveling in his secretive existence.

"Yet you speak of it now, in front of me?" I queried.

"There are no more than six men who know my true purpose. You are the seventh. This knowledge alone, places my life at risk," he offered forward.

"Why should you endanger yourself by telling *me* this?" I asked, completely mystified.

"For years I have been content to supply funds to movements who've had Israel's true interests at heart. This way, I didn't have to make myself known and avoided any direct conflict with the Procurate. Now, events have greatly changed." He paused as if having second thoughts about saying more.

"Changed? In what way?" I prompted. He thought for a moment and then continued.

"I always kept a distance from your family - just in case. I also became more involved in Temple politics - more can be achieved from inside the system than out."

"What's the Temple got to do with this? Are they active with the resistance?" I asked, barely able to believe the possibility, since they derived their unquestioned power from Rome.

"No!" he answered vehemently. "But they have the direct ear of the Procurate General - an unHoly alliance! They have fallen into bed with the Roman whore. The Romans allow them to apply the law in any way they see fit - as long as there's no civil insurrection and they encourage our people to pay the Roman taxes."

"So the people are expected to pay the Roman *and* Temple taxes?"

"Look around," he offered. "Everywhere you see our own people begging - because they can't find enough for even a single tax, let alone two. We need a true King, Yeshua - one that will stand up to the Sanhedrin."

"But I thought Herod's son was still on our throne?"

"Only in name. His official title is Tetrarch - but a Rose by any other name is still - King. After so many uprisings, the Caesars did tire of him and he was banished. Unfortunately, the Romans needed a figurehead for purposes of State - so he has returned." To show his disgust, Joseph spat on the floor.

"So who do the people look to now?" I asked.

"The Sanhedrin - they rule the Temple. I've come to know the High Priest Caiaphas quite well."

"And is he one of these six you mention?"

Joseph looked horrified. "Certainly not! If he knew, you would now be talking to a dead man. His hand fits neatly into the Roman glove. It's a bitter pill for the Romans to swallow, but they have to eat?" He paced for a few moments before continuing. "It's taken many years and a lot of sacrifice, but I may soon be elected to the council. There, my influence may be greater than all the weapons I've supplied over the years. The Sanhedrin even supported the instigation of Jewish collectors for the Roman tax."

"Jews collecting Roman taxes?" I spoke in disbelief. Joseph smiled as he nodded in agreement.

"Very clever really," he explained. "The collector pays Rome a set fee - which is one fifth of the taxes due. The collector then does all the work of collection for the Romans and is allowed to keep the difference."

"And if people refuse, or can't pay?"

"Either their lands are taken from them, which is most common; or they are faced with the full weight of Roman Law -and can end up in the belly of a slave-ship. The collectors are less than Gentiles!"

"Again, I ask you - what's this got to do with me? What's so important that it can't be discussed in front of my own flesh and blood?" I asked, seeing that he was having difficulty in directly answering. He extended his arms and rested them on my shoulders.

"Because Israel looks for a Messiah - a man to lead an army against the might of Rome." His words were stark, but clear. The suggestion was so ridiculous I had to consciously stop myself from laughing.

"But we've had so many Messiahs and where has it got us? And I'm no soldier!"

Joseph continued undeterred. "What you say is true - there have been many Messiahs. But what I ask you Yeshua is, how many have carried the blood of David in their veins - and been educated in the ways of the world?"

"I haven't been trained in the ways of war," I pointed out, stating the obvious. I couldn't outright reject my Uncle, since I could see the depth and seriousness of his suggestion.

"You don't need to know the ways," he spoke, apparently encouraged by my response. "We have men who have trained in the hills of Galilee, since the time of Herod's banishment. They've trained for nothing else these past years. The Sanhedrin remain comfortable under Roman rule, so they can't be trusted with this information. We've infiltrated the homes of the Roman Governor - we have access to the Legion's movements...."

"But, the might of Rome?" I countered. "And how do you know I'll have any part of it anyway?" He seemed pained at my words as if he had no contingent plan.

"That's why we're speaking privately, Yeshua. The family have no idea."

"But why me? Any one of my brothers would be more suitable and they've worked with you in the yards. They're known."

"You've traveled in foreign lands, Yeshua. You have seen how others live. You must recognize the tyranny of Rome?" he spoke with a note of exasperation setting into his voice.

"That's true - and I'm sure my brothers recognize it even better than me..."

"Yeshua, Yeshua," he interrupted, as if I hadn't heard him correctly. "It's true your entire family *is* in the line of King David, but it's *because* they're known that we can't use them. You have been away. There's a mystique about your travels and the men who taught you. That's what we need - a charismatic leader! How can we ask thousands to risk their lives following orders from a man that only days earlier, they worked along side of - and was as ordinary as they are? No, we need someone extraordinary, someone who is removed from their everyday existence. Someone who holds the right to the Judaean throne!" Joseph stopped as though no further argument were needed.

"You'd put me on Herod's throne?" I asked in disbelief. I couldn't be certain if that was a compliment or an insult.

"The throne isn't his by right," Joseph snapped back, revealing his personal hatred for the man. "This way, we would have a true Jewish King," he justified.

"But I've no desire to rule."

"You wouldn't have to! The King rules through the Sanhedrin - and he names the leader of the Temple."

"And that would be?" I voiced the words so that I could hear it from Joseph's own lips.

"That would be me," he answered without reservation or modesty. I nodded my head in understanding - neither agreeing or disagreeing. I stepped out of the room and let the evening breeze touch my face. Joseph's words have become oppressive and I need to breathe fresh air.

"What's your answer, Yeshua?" he spoke, remaining inside the room. My brothers stood grouped beside the wine-table and looked inquisitively towards me, sensing something was amiss.   I smiled and waved away their concerns.

"If I refuse?"

"Then Israel will have to wait for a Jew with courage," he spoke coming out into the light.   "And I will no longer recognize my brother's family!"   His expression must have been fierce, because I could see by James' reaction that this wasn't a demeanor he had shown before.

"The sword of Damocles never shone so bright," I spoke under my breath.

"I didn't hear your answer, Yeshua," Joseph came round to face me.

"I didn't give it," I answered evenly, looking him straight in the eye.   A man of his influence was evidently not used to this equality of nature and he became flustered.

"You will - I *will* have your answer!"

In order to save him further embarrassment, since we were being closely watched, I answered.

"Before I give you a decision, I have to return to Egypt.   I have important - unfinished - business to attend to."

Turning away in frustration Joseph suddenly saw the attention our meeting was attracting.   He smiled warmly to allay the concerned and watchful eyes.

"Then we *both* have unfinished business.   When you return for your wedding - Israel will have your answer."   With those words, he casually threw his cloak around his shoulders and brusquely left.

Mother came quickly over, seeing Joseph leave.

"Where's your Uncle going?" she asked, concerned.

"He's received important news and has to return to the coast."

"But he's had no food - or drink!" she protested.

"And with all this - you've remembered a child's delight for cold figs," I spoke, taking one from the dish she carried and putting an arm around her narrow shoulders.   She would have questioned me further about Joseph but, being complimented on something she had gone to great lengths to assure, she was distracted from her previous concern.

The following day, before the sun had risen, I arrived in Jerusalem and headed for the animal market. The camel trader was happy to conclude his first transaction before he had even eaten breakfast. I bought basic provisions and as the sun crested the Judaean hills, I felt it's first warm rays on my back. My destination was less than a month's travel. I could have taken the boat from Askalon to Alexandria, which would have shortened the journey considerably, but I felt the need to be totally alone. The desert was always so healing. No man-made structures distracted the mind and I could be at home in eternity. The route was well worn along the coast and not difficult to follow. Beyond Gaza, the stony scrubland gave way to soft shores and lapping sea. Even the camel felt energized and I often allowed it to gallop of its own accord. Although I encouraged it to enter the cool waters of the sea, it tried to bite at my feet in objection. Perhaps moisture trapped the soil in it's hooves, which it had remembered painfully from some previous occasion? Heading south across the Sinai, I only traveled at night. By day I sought what little shade the desert offered, which was only a few sparse palm trees hidden in the wadis. The camel was happy enough just to remain stationary beneath the blazing sun.

The Temple of Zoan was exactly as I had remembered it twenty-odd years earlier. The monolithic rectangle of the Temple seemed to grow like some huge axle that had thrust itself up from the inner mechanism of the blood-red sand. While it was not a natural formation, it seemed to be the creative force from which the natural surrounding area drew it's purpose.

Before darkness had fallen, I arrived at the outer walls.

Apparently I had been observed at some distance away and food and wine had already been prepared.

"Don't you know me, Ruth?" I asked on recognizing her face.

She had aged considerably. Her jet-black hair was now entirely silver and one side of her face was paralyzed from a past stroke. She moved closer to see. Her eyes suddenly lit up with recognition.

"I do remember a year when the date harvest was less than it should have been. And I do remember two well-fed young boys that had come from Judaea and ate less than they should at the table."

She smiled as I remembered how John and I would shake down the ripe dates before anyone else was awake.

"It is a wise, or hungry, woman who can recall her accounting, after so many years," I countered.

She came forward and kissed me warmly on both cheeks. "How is your dear mother?"

"She's well."

"And John the Date Eater?" she asked, smiling.

"I must confess, I don't know. I've been traveling abroad for many years and have heard that he lives with the wild animals in the mountains. He's become quite famous."

"How things have changed. My husband passed away eight years ago and since, I've become the High Priest," she spoke with sorrow at his passing.

"A woman High Priest?" I queried.

"Yes, a woman. Do you find that so strange?" she asked without taking offense.

"Forgive my surprise. It's just that in the Temple....."

"Ah, the Temple," she concluded. "Steeped in tradition - its strength and it's great weakness." She spoke as if from a far deeper understanding than she was prepared to elaborate on. I didn't press further but would dearly have liked to.

"But you say you've traveled for many years? Where have you visited and what have you learned," she asked settling down beside me.

"Where to begin! I traveled with a wonderful Prince from India. He showed me true friendship and took me to many of his country's wisest men."

"But what did you learn, that you should come again to Zoan? Even the Bedou rarely visit and traders don't even know of its existence," she prompted.

"I learned that without love, nothing exists or has its being. I learned that love for one, is love for all. I learned that love is the true face of God."

"Then you have learned in a few short years what many Initiates have taken lifetimes to learn. This was no small journey you've undertaken," she spoke, wiping a tear from my face, which I hadn't even been aware of. Now that I was older, I noticed how close to tears I became whenever I broached the profound or looked at anything of beauty. In that beauty I saw God's hand, openly visible.

"We've heard of their great skill in healing?" she prompted, wanting to hear specifics.

"It's true, they have great wisdom in that area. A great soul told me that everything in this world is as it should be and that disease is discord with nature - which can only be truly healed by the heart. I was taught many Yogic techniques, the highest form of healing being thought - directed only by love. As long as our attention is placed on the Holy Father, no harm can attend the healer. However, if the Ego directs the healing, a debt must be paid by the healer and many healers don't live out their full years." My thoughts returned to Udraka and the gentleness of his teaching. Ruth agreed, silently sensing my sadness at leaving India.

"And are there specific meanings behind each type of illness?" she asked, as if for confirmation.

"I was told that for each illness there *is* a specific lesson. What the lesson might be, can only be understood by the person themselves - they have to meditate on it. It's the body's method of communicating a spiritual message or principal. That's why an illness has to be loved and not fought. By love we communicate, by fighting we develop a resistance to the voice of Spirit."

"So illness is the result of our disobeying a Universal principle?" she suggested.

"Denied, or neglected. Man has fallen into the illusion, that we aren't fully conscious and are consequently not responsible. Our true self is ever awake and all knowing - there are no victims!"

"But you've seen the children of the poor," she objected. "Even in our own country, peasants have mutilated their children so that they can have better success with begging. What child has ever asked to go hungry? How can you say there are no victims?" I realized how callous my words might sound, but I had to speak what I knew to be true.

"The oppressed have been the oppressors in previous lives. The hungry have known excess - and deliberately squandered it. Soul chooses to know these lessons."

"We judge ourselves?"

"It has always been this way. Former Kings and Queens now wait at our table. The first shall be last and the last shall be first."

"Should we have sympathy for their situation, since it is self - or rather, Soul imposed?" she asked with deepest interest.

"Sympathy comes from the head. We should have compassion. Compassion comes from the heart, recognizing it has also experienced this same lesson in previous lives."

"There but for the grace of God go I?" she inquired.

"No. There by the grace of God, I have *been*."

"I'd like to learn more. Will you stay long?" she inquired. It wasn't until that moment that I realized my journey didn't end in Zoan.

"I wish I could, but time nips eagerly at my heels - the time has come." Even as I spoke these strange words, I knew that Ruth understood exactly their meaning.

"There has been an anxiousness throughout our land - a trembling. Only a few of the Initiates have recognized its true meaning. For the past month, a few of us have fasted, in anticipation of who was to come. I fear for you Yeshua!" My old self was eager to ask 'fear for what'? The Higher Self I now knew to be my true being, asked nothing. The consciousness that had brought me to this point, wanted nothing of the 'known'. This was a time that had never been before and no other consciousness had walked the path in just this way. No matter how kindly Ruth's words might be meant, they could only be hollow and without meaning.

"The time has come to prepare for the Silent Brotherhood. If ever I needed your Love, sweet Ruth, it's now."

She took both my hands in hers and tears fell from her cheeks as she looked into my face.

"If you are to go to Giza - then from this day forward our doors shall be closed and our eye single upon your purpose. We fear for you Yeshua - and for mankind." She stood up and tenderly kissed me on the forehead. Without further word, she turned away and went to pray in the temple. Without any words being spoken, the entire community quietly followed, even those who had still been working in the fields. The huge wooden doors resonated loudly as they shut behind the last person. I remained sitting there for several hours watching showers of shooting stars in the clear night sky. Pulling my cloak close against the cold of the desert air, a shiver ran through me as I thought of the path ahead.

At first light, I regained my camel and headed further into the desert. This time I followed no known route. Where a wadi meandered, I followed. Where a bird glided silently upon a warm current, I followed. Where the cresting line of a dune pointed, I followed. God's hand was everywhere.

At night the jackals called close by. I lay close against the belly of my camel. With it's back to the wind, I was protected. On several occasions, venomous and deadly creatures curled up close to us, so that they too should share our warmth. I felt to be in the center of God's outstretched palm. I was safe.

One night as I stared up at the nearly full moon, I heard a loud and distinct voice that I barely recognized.

"There is a silence that can be heard, where Soul may meet its God and there is found the fountain of wisdom," the voice spoke. I jumped up and looked around, but there was no one there. The camel shambled to its feet, wondering why I had made such a sudden move. It also looked around. I patted its flank to calm it. The animal snorted loudly in complaint and then settled back down.

"All who enter here are filled with light, and love speaks through them," the voice continued. "This is the secret place where God talks directly to man. This silence cannot be understood and is only heard by the heart. You have brought yourself to this place Yeshua, now prepare for the World."

To recognize that familiarity of voice I had to go back to my youth and the stranger who was called Maitreya. I rarely saw his face. He arrived at night and spoke with my mother in hushed tones and was always gone before dawn   There was no mistaking the warm reassurance of that voice - it was Maitreya.

I called his name loud into the open desert, but there was no reply.

The following evening, I crested a large sand dune and there it was - the Great Pyramid of Giza! My heart leapt, beating so powerfully that I wondered at it's strength. Breath came in short excited gasps. What a dazzling sight it was! Brightly lit by the full moon, a warm golden light reflected from it's upper surface. The golden triangle at its peak, pointed heavenwards - the Trinity! Two smaller pyramids lay in the background, but neither had the majestic presence of the Great Pyramid. The lush vegetation at it's base spread deep into the desert and all the way west to the Nile. I had heard many stories about these almost mythical stones, but none did them justice. The energy which radiated and fed the surrounding environment, was tangible. I passed my hand in front of my face to see if the effect of the energy was diminished - it wasn't. The ancient manuscripts of Leh spoke of visitors from another constellation directing the construction of these wonderful monuments. I was well aware of the power of Tantra, but I could hardly believe mere sound being responsible for moving such huge blocks. My thoughts returned to the levitating Yogi and his feat with the boulder.

In the foreground, I saw my final destination. Enigmatically looking back towards me, was the Sphinx! I thought of the message given many years earlier.

"The courage of a lion and a mother's love - embodied in stone," I whispered to myself, remembering Tyagi Baba's message.

I dismounted and gazed at the wonderful scene in front of me. The camel looked to see if we were to make camp.

"We've traveled far together my fine friend and you've served me well," I spoke as he watched. "It's time for you to be honored by your friends." With a firm smack on his hind leg, I sent him trotting off into the night. Moments later he returned, confused. Our journey together had ended - mine, just begun.

"Go!" I shouted. "Join your friends. Where my footsteps lead, even I fear to tread." Again he looked at me and then, as if reaching a decision, turned away towards the lush green plain below.

My journey had been long and I wanted to be aware of each footstep that took me closer to my fate. The powder-soft sand of the dunes soon gave way to the firm cultivated area surrounding the pyramids.

I arrived at the base of the Sphinx just as the first pink rays of dawn began to banish the distant stars. Standing between the great paws of the lion, I could now see just how monumental a task it must have been, to create such a magnificent structure. From where I had first seen it, it hadn't appeared anything like as large - being dwarfed by the vast scale of the Great Pyramid. The silver light of the moon played at the corners of the fine half-closed eyes of the monolith, impassively staring out to the desert beyond. In the distance I heard a dog barking. It gave me a curious anchor on reality.

Feeling strongly drawn towards the rising stone chest, I noticed a door, finely outlined in the silver light. As I stepped onto the flat stone pediment, two huge doors swung silently inward to reveal an inner chamber. Stepping up to the threshold, the earth tremored and a shower of fine sand fell from the head of the Sphinx.

"What's the meaning of this?" a resonant voice called out from the inner darkness. "There's nothing here for thieves!" A veil was drawn back to reveal seven darkly-hooded figures, sat around a circular table. On the walls, flaming bulrushes cast dancing shadows.

"I'm no thief!" I called back.

"Yet you enter as such, in darkness?"

"My name is Yeshua ben Joseph," I called out.

"I've heard of such a name," the speaker answered. "Is he also known as Jesus in the land of the Greeks?"

"I am called such. I'm a Nazarene and live far to the West," I answered, surprised that my name should be known.

"Then, besides being a thief, you must also be a liar, because such a man wouldn't come in such a way - in the dead of night," he dismissed.

"He would - and does - come; unseen and without trumpet," I abruptly answered.

The group consulted briefly, before the speaker again spoke. "If you are this Jesus, what would you want from us?" he asked as if this were a riddle that held a key. "We are old and care less for the affairs of men."

"I ask.... ," immediately I spoke, I knew I had used the wrong words. "No, I *demand* my birthright!"

"As I said, we have nothing to give. Demands can only be made where there is something to...."

"Forgive me elder brother, but I've learned in dreams that you are keepers of the Sacred Flame," I interrupted, unable to resist an uncomfortable agitation that threatened to explode from my lower spine.

"You're mistaken, young Rabbi," he answered crisply. "The only flames we have, are those you see around you. It's little enough, but you're welcome to choose whichever you prefer." He gestured generously towards the licking flame of the bulrushes.

The agitation, or perhaps it was light, spread higher up my spine making me even more uncomfortable and ill at ease.

"The flame I seek, is hidden deep within the heart of all men." I spoke the words and they sounded like echoes, even as they left my lips. One of the elders drew back the hooded cowl to reveal she was an old Ethiopian woman. Although of great age, her beauty was breath-taking and her every movement exuded a deep serenity.

"If this flame is in all men, then why do you seek our help?" she asked. "Choose any man and leave us to our ways."

"Because," I answered her directly as I approached the table, and unable to wait for an invitation, "in my mind's eye, I have come to know that you sit as guardians to my father's house."

"You speak of the Great Pyramid?" the first speaker dubiously asked.

"Yes," I addressed the assembly as I walked around them. "I have dreamed this day of standing before you and undertaking the test of the Christ Consciousness!"

There was an awkward silence, as though they expected me to say more. I had said all that I felt was necessary and waited for one of them to respond. The others looked to the first speaker. He drew back his cowl and I could see he was an Albino. His hair fell slightly lower than his shoulders and was as white as the Himalayan snows. His eyes were the palest blue.

"I believe it may be as you say - you are the Rabbi Jesus," he began. "Unfortunately, you're mistaken. No man would willingly ask to be put to such a terrible test!"

"My will is lost in love of my father in Heaven. I now have memory of many lives that prepared me for this moment. Every atom in my body burns with an intense and cold fire." At these words the woman suddenly threw a look towards the first speaker.

"A cold fire?" he questioned.

"So cold, it's beyond Mind and description," I answered sensing a door open.

"And what about your heart?" the woman quietly asked.

"My heart is like any other's - it trembles with the greatest dread for what I now ask."

The assembly exchanged glances as if sharing a communication. Once agreed, the assembly looked to the first speaker to deliver their verdict.

"Hold to your silence, Rabbi. As Elder Brothers, we will join our hearts with Divine Love and you will have your answer." With these words, the seven elders joined hands and bowed their heads forward in prayer. In the semi-darkness, the last man to bow his head was much younger than the others and had a strange knowing and familiarity about him. I dropped to my knees and prayed to the Divine Spirit in all things.

After a short time, the lead spokesperson looked up.

"Rabbi from the Himalayas, do you still ask to be put to the test of the Christ Consciousness?" The others remained with their heads forward in prayer.

"For this and many lives before, I ask the right to be put to your most severe test," I answered.

"Again I say, you don't know what you ask, perhaps..!"

"I've traveled among many peoples and seen their suffering. If I'm to be of any service in removing some of that pain, I must know the depths to which man can fall." As I spoke, the others raised their heads and pushed back their cowls so that I should be able to identify them. "Outwardly I've made little show, but destiny demands.... Formally I ask, show me your darkest and most dismal crypts, so that I may truly know my father's will!"

"I am Bethsheba," the old Ethiopian announced. "We respect your Judaic beliefs, but I beg you to reconsider - you may be wrongly called?"

"If I am mistaken, then God isn't in each grain of desert sand, nor is he in the hidden rainbow of morning dew. No, I have dreamed that this council sits at the doorway of inner worlds unimagined by Judaic or any other religion." I was prepared to say no more. The grouped elders saw that I couldn't be dissuaded and turned to speak quietly among themselves.

The younger of the group, the one I felt had a strange familiarity about him, then stood up to speak. Suddenly I recognized him - it was Maitreya! Some charismatic force had kept my attention on the first speaker and I hadn't been able to focus on any of the others, except the woman called Bethsheba. A few hours earlier I would have called out in relief at recognizing his face, yet now I felt it inappropriate - and unnecessary. In all these years, he had barely aged. His hair was now silver, but his face still resembled the young tutor that had come secretively to teach my mother.

"You have dreamed well, Yeshua," he spoke with great warmth. "But how will you pay for this service?"

His question took me by surprise. "There is only one coin of any value," I answered.

"But there are so many currencies."

"Not in Spirit," I answered. "There is only one true coin - eternal Soul."

He was taken aback by my words and hesitated before speaking. "You offer 'eternal Soul'? Again, I must echo my brother's concern - you don't know what you ask, or offer."

"And what do you know of 'eternal Soul'?" Bethsheba gently interrupted.

"It cannot be *known*," I answered. "It can only be experienced." Bethsheba looked to Maitreya as if to apologize for interrupting his line of questioning. A kind look from him suggested she shouldn't concern herself with etiquette and that she had spoken where necessary. Then I realized by their body language, everyone deferred to him. His eyes met mine and I knew he had read my thoughts, and smiled. Maitreya sat back down, indicating that the first speaker should continue.

"You have answered well, young Rabbi," he began formally addressing the assembly in general. "Now, if you still wish to face the terror of Dark Oblivion, you must take your leave of this outer world."

"I still wish it," I answered, feeling a cold sweat covering my chest and back.

"I am the Hierophant of the assembly of Melchizedek, and it is my responsibility to point out the Sacred Geometry," he spoke, indicating fine mathematical symbols carved into the stone walls. I hadn't been aware of them before, but now they stood out in clear relief. As with Maitreya, they had been invisible to my eye until this moment.

"Everyone and everything must have his sound and his symbol," he continued. "The circle is the symbol of the perfect man and twelve is his number. This Hebrew," he addressed the assembly, "will test the circle. If he fails, the shame will be ours and the world will be without light."

The Hierophant clapped his hands and a tall Nubian warrior stepped forward out of the shadows. The Nubian had darker skin than even the people of Southern India. A broad scimitar hung from a sash at his hip. In his outstretched arms, he held a large shallow-based dish on which rested a small vase of precious oils, a sprig of herbs and a crystal bladed knife. Handing the dish to the Hierophant, the Nubian returned to the darker shadows. The dish was ceremoniously passed around the table. Each person held it a moment, before passing it to their left. Finally it came to Bethsheba. As she received it, her eyes rolled up into her head and she stood blindly up, as if held by some unseen but cogent force. Although very old, she moved towards me with the step of a much younger woman. I remained kneeling. Standing directly in front of me, Bethsheba's eyes dropped down to their normal position. Using the sprig of herbs, she sprinkled water on the crown of my head. Then, taking the knife and dipping it in the oils, the figure of a cross was traced across my forehead. A look in her eyes suggested there was something she desperately wanted me to know, but was afraid to communicate. The Nubian, again stepped forward and helped me to my feet. A gesture from the Hierophant indicated I should follow the warrior. The chamber went considerably further back inside the Sphinx than I could have imagined. Holding a burning rush, the Nubian held it high so that I should see the vast tapestry of geometric designs as we passed. They were of a manner and style that I had never encountered before, yet contained information that registered with me at a deeper level than consciousness. Much information related to the origins of man and his connection with the greater Universe. As I passed, I became aware of how manipulated Mankind's genetic memory had become. At the end of the great hall, a tapestry concealed a small and perfectly concealed door. With the slightest of pressures, the door swung open to reveal descending stairs. The stairs spiraled gently downwards and beyond the flickering light.

Before entering the stairwell, I stopped to look back. The assembled group looked anxious. Bethsheba went to get up from the table, but Maitreya put a restraining hand on her arm. There was something she desperately wanted to tell me.

"Where does this lead?" I asked.

The Nubian looked at me coldly and answered without emotion. "To the depths where men's thoughts cannot reach." He turned and lead the way down the stone stairs. I followed a little behind, since his lean body caste a dark shadow at my feet and the stairs began to fall away sharply. As we descended, the high ceiling gradually lowered, such that I had to lean slightly backward or risk grazing my forehead. The sound of our sandals slapping against the cold stone echoed into the descending tunnel, but didn't return.

"How long will I stay?" I asked, half hoping that the sound of my voice might give a clue as to how much further we had to travel.

"As long as the Council decides is necessary," he spoke, preferring to remain silent. After we had descended at least a hundred feet and the air had become foul, the steps began to level out, entering a more open area. The Nubian stopped and offered forward the burning brand, indicating that I should proceed ahead. He fell quietly into step behind me. Soon I was confronted with a broad and clean-cut rock face into which was cut the relief of thirteen identical doors. Around the stone frames, pale blue stones depicted the story of Osiris and Isis. Each door had the left eye of Horus carved into its stone fascia. I stopped and looked questioningly towards my companion. He looked blankly back at me, suggesting that I should know how to proceed. I was about to approach the nearest door, when I realized how right he was. If I was to be worthy of the test of the Christ Consciousness, then I should be able to intuit which was the correct path to take. Allowing my mind to become silent, I felt inexorably drawn to the seventh door. I stepped forward and pressed against the cold eye. The stone door swung weightlessly inward. Relieved, I turned to see my companion returning the scimitar to the sash at his hip.

"And if I had chosen the wrong door?" I asked in shocked amazement.

"Your head would now be parted from your shoulders," he evenly answered. He smiled encouragingly, so that we should proceed. I returned the brand to him and he lead the way through the door.

For a short distance we traveled along a narrow corridor whose ceiling was so high, that the light from the burning brand barely reached it. Finally we came up against a roughly hewn rock face. The torch illuminated a small irregular opening of approximately four feet high and very narrow.

"We're here," he simply stated. Being so tall, it would be very difficult for the Nubian to enter. He lit a fresh torch and handed it to me. "You're smaller, you should go first."

I bent forward and entered what was a short tunnel of perhaps six feet in length. I had to hold the torch at arm's length in front of me or the heat would have singed my hair, given the confined space. Ahead, the floor suddenly dropped fifteen feet to a small cavern which appeared to be man-made and more or less rectangular. Against the far wall, I could just see several steps lead down into a small formal pool of water.

As I wondered how we should descend, I felt a strong push from behind. Falling blindly out into the darkness, I landed on my right shoulder. Although I fell heavily, the ground was covered in centuries of accumulated dust and I did little more than graze my wrists and hip. The light from the torch beside me, illuminated the Nubian's broad grin, high above.

"Welcome to your new kingdom, King of the Jews!" he laughed. "At least you have a light to survey your subjects!" His laughter could still be heard, long after the nimbus of his torch had vanished from the passage ceiling. I sat for some moments trying to adjust to this sudden change of circumstance. Against the wall to my left, two perfectly preserved skeletons leaned against each other. Judging by the dust that covered the leg bones, it had been a long time since this couple had breathed their last. Picking up the flaming torch, I took a closer inspection of my 'room-mates'. The larger figure had an amulet hanging around its neck. The graven image showed Tantric symbols that I was familiar with from India. Taking the light to the water pool, I inspected the steps closely. Where the rest of this enclosure was roughly cut, the steps by contrast, were exactly fashioned with fine tracery at their edges. Having worked alongside my father, I knew how many hard months this fine stone crafting would have taken. The three steps disappeared into the inky darkness of the pool. Cupping my hand slightly, I determined the water was fresh, though strongly tinged with minerals.

Trying to assess the situation before the torch burnt out, it was quickly apparent that there was only one way out of this enclosure and that was at least fifteen feet above me. Worn segments below the threshold showed where previous occupants had desperately tried to climb out. The surface of the rock, although roughly-hewn gave no purchase hold. In the failing light I was forced to consider the possibility that I had, in fact, been buried alive. Given the staleness of the air and the realization of my situation, my heart beat faster and my breaths came in short gasps. I no longer had the reassurance of spiritual certainty. This faith that had carried me through so many dangers was found wanting and I felt shame - and fear. Could I possibly have hung my whole existence on an illusion of Spirit? Inwardly I called out to God, but all remained silent and unchanged.

I was confronted with two choices. One: have faith in Man and wait for my release; or two: have faith in Spirit that had lead me to this dismal crypt buried deep beneath the desert sands. No man would have any reason to come searching for a stranger deep within the heart of the earth, so the argument for Man held little sway. Spirit on the other hand had never failed me. In short, I had no alternative but to prepare myself for whatever test was intended.

Leaning the burning torch up against the steps, I returned to sit beneath the passageway. The only indication of time I would have, was the torch; after that, I'd have no way of knowing.

As the failing light began to sputter, I closed my eyes in meditation. Even with my eyelids shut, I was aware of the final glimmer of light disappearing from the dark tomb. After a period of time which may have been minutes, it may have been hours - it may even have been days; I opened my eyes. A light still glowed over by the water's edge. I stood up to see if I could fan the embers of the torch back into flame. Approaching the water, it became evident that the light I had seen, wasn't coming from the long extinguished brand, but from deep within the water itself. There didn't appear to be a specific source for the light. I presumed it hadn't been apparent before, because of the overpowering light from the bulrush. Even then, its pale glow could be mistaken for a trick of the eye. Looking to the side of it, as you would a distant star, it appeared the light source was creeping in from some deep cavern beyond this immediate pool. I sat for some moments at the water's edge before deciding on a course of action.

Stripping down to my loin cloth, I prepared to dive down. The Yogic training I had received, would serve me well now. Slowing my heart beat, I took several deep breaths before submerging myself in the cold water. Swimming down to the depth of two men standing, I came across a narrow horizontal passageway from where the light appeared to be coming. Quickly deciding to investigate, I swam further into the passageway. I had traveled about ten feet, when I saw the narrow opening above. It appeared that this was where the light originated. The gap was little wider than the span of two hands, but just wide enough for me to squeeze through, with some difficulty. Excited, I unintentionally allowed my heartbeat to accelerate and headed upward. Just before coming up into the larger pool, I suddenly saw, ten feet or more above me, several huge Nile crocodiles. Their dark silhouettes were frenziedly tearing apart the remains of a donkey. Terrified, I quickly retreated back along my narrow passageway - but not before one of the large creatures noticed my movement and dived down to investigate. With my lungs at bursting point, I desperately swam back towards the darkness of my original enclosure. I hoped with all my heart, that the fissure joining the lower passage and the other pool, would be too narrow for the crocodile to follow. As I broke the surface of the entry pool, my head pounded so painfully that I fully expected my skull to burst. Getting out of the water as fast as I could, I watched to see if I had been followed. My eyes strained to see if the pale light became blocked my some reptilian pursuer. After some minutes it seemed I hadn't. However, what I couldn't be sure of, was that the crocodile hadn't accessed the lower passage and was now waiting patiently for me to return.

I sat back against the rock and tried to solve the riddle. It had to be a riddle? Surely Spirit wouldn't have lead me all this way, simply so that I should end my days in the stomach of those cold-blooded creatures?! I decided to rest a while and then try again, even if the crocodile was waiting. I had read about Daniel in the lion's den - but that was scripture and this was the real world! If I was to escape this enclosure, it would have to be by my own efforts. In my heart, I rationalized that any divine intervention would invalidate the trial I had chosen to undertake. So I would enter the water again and pray that I escape the jaws of those terrifying reptiles.

Going to the water's edge, I dived head-first this time, determined to control my heartbeat whatever happened. The effort to reach the second pool seemed easier this time. Two crocodiles alerted by my earlier intrusion, circled in readiness above. The water was lightly clouded by the blood of the now vanished donkey, yet still the reptiles spotted my movement. Suddenly I realized that my arm had been lacerated when I had panicked, returning to the passage earlier, and it was this blood that had alerted the creatures. With several powerful sweeps of their tails, the crocodiles dived quickly towards me and tried to enter the passageway - without success. Two tried to gain access at the same time. The larger of the two, spurred on by the scent of my blood, bit deep into the throat of the other crocodile. Suddenly the water was awash with blood, slashing teeth and thrashing tails. The force of their horrifying struggle pushed me backward in the tunnel. There was no way I was going to be able to get past these terrifying and rapacious creatures. About to retrace my route, I noticed an area of even deeper darkness further on into the tunnel. In the instant I recognized that this might lead to another possible opening, I was faced with an unimaginable choice. I could return to the original enclosure, or go deeper to investigate the darkness - a course which, if I was wrong, would seal my fate in this cold watery grave. Having only the option of being torn apart by these savage creatures, or slowly starving to death, I decided to swim forward past them, towards a possible dark oblivion. My lungs ached painfully and wouldn't sustain me enough for a return journey - I had passed the point of no return. Passing only inches beneath the thrusting and razored teeth, I headed deeper down towards the darkness. Passing under a projecting rock, I suddenly perceived a distant glimmer of light. With my breath exhausted, I opened my mouth to allow the water in, desperately hoping that I might gain some oxygen from the water. The passageway started to descend slightly, but then took an abrupt turn upward towards the light.

I broke the surface like a bobbing cork, choking from the water and my head pounding with intense pain. Momentarily I saw that I had entered a well-lit and marbled room - before passing into unconsciousness and comforting darkness.

When I awoke, I found myself half in the water and half lying on the carved steps - similar to those in the original cavern. The walls, I had originally taken for marble, were in fact some translucent material from which a rose-colored light emanated. Seeing the light emitted from all walls, there appeared to be no exit other that by which I had entered. Again I was trapped! By now I was forced to recognize that my strength wouldn't be enough to carry me back to the first chamber, so I faced the very real probability of starving to death. How desperate, to be buried alive - and forgotten!

Whether I passed into unconsciousness again, I couldn't tell. In front of my inner vision, distorted and terrifying images of the damned presented themselves and I felt the cold grasp of oblivion seize my chest. Endlessly more fantastic images and ogres of terror flew in my face, screaming and tearing at my very soul. Whatever part of my consciousness was able to observe this endless nightmare, was blasted into a million shards of light, so that there was no more observation. Whatever had previously been identified with the I, merged totally with the golden light beyond - there was no separation, on any level. The light was beyond any experienced in the physical world, this simply was. In that tangible light, love was total and without limitation. I had truly come home.

"Jesus the Jew," a voice sounded from an infinite distance. I felt a resistance to recognition and my body jerked involuntarily as my consciousness slammed back into the chest. Cool, fresh air washed over my face and consciousness slowly returned. "Are you there?" the voice I now identified as Bethsheba's spoke. I opened my eyes with the greatest reluctance, to find I was still in the land of the living.

"Still here and alive," I barely whispered.

"Come quickly," she urged.

"Does the Hierophant call me?" I asked, adjusting my eyes to the bright light.

"No, and he won't. I beg you forgive me. It's taken this long to slip away without being noticed. Come quickly!"

"The council doesn't call me?" I asked, confused at her agitation.

"I've got horses ready" she continued as she helped me to my feet. "There isn't much time before they realize I've gone."

"But, I'm not called?" I blindly repeated.

"Jesus, the Council of Seven has no intention of allowing you to leave this chamber alive," she spoke as slowly as her urgency would allow.   "You were to be starved or eaten by the crocodiles. Now come! We must go!"

"But I'm to be tested?"

"You were never meant to leave this terrible crypt. I wanted to warn you, but I'd have joined you if I had spoken out," she answered.

"I can't leave.   I gave my word that I would undertake the test," I spoke recognizing her confusion.

"This *isn't* a test. A messenger has already been sent to claim the reward for your death. Hurry, there's no time, we must go now," she spoke pulling at my arm.

Although considerably weakened, I shrugged off her hold and stood back - or rather, fell away.

"I've given my word!"

"What good is the word of a dead Rabbi to those that continue to suffer in the outer world?   - And an agreement made with liars is not binding on either side," she desperately reasoned.

"If words are as cheap as the wind, then the soul has no compass. My words were spoken with thoughts of God. If others have no concern for the effect of their words, I can't be their judge. My breath is God's and I've undertaken the test in his name - I can't leave."

She held up a hand to silence me. "Someone's coming. Hurry before it's too late. They'll kill us both!"

"Return to the world Bethsheba. Thank you for your loving kindness. If I am to die, God wishes me here and that's my bond."

"Farewell good Jew, because we won't see each other again in this life," she hurriedly whispered, leaving by a small door in the corner of the room. The door shut and no suggestion of it's existence remained - the surface of the wall was again flawless.

I had been left to die - or I would be put to the test of the Christ consciousness.   I lay down on the bare floor and fell into a deep sleep.

In that sleep of death, a blinding light startled me into an unrecognized form of consciousness, such that I couldn't determine if it were bitter or sweet. Slowly, the state became modified so that I could recognize human forms approaching.

"Arise Jesus the Christ, for you have passed the Dark Night of Soul," the voice I knew to be the Hierophant's spoke. "Prepare to be the Anointed One!"

Bethsheba lead the assembled group, each now dressed in long purple robes and carrying flaming torches.   Beside the six High Priests, six further priest and Priestess', also dressed in purple robes, lead me from the tomb and into a narrow vaulted passageway. After a short walk and my senses gradually returning, we came to a white-marbled wall in which a low passageway was perfectly cut. Several other passageways also converged at this point. The assembly stood aside so that I should continue, alone.

"It is the Brotherhood's greatest honor to have sealed the destiny of the Nazarene," the Hierophant humbly spoke, urging me forward. The ceiling of the passageway was so low that, had it not been inclined upward, I would have been forced to stoop. Although there was no light in the tunnel, a fresh breeze on my face came as welcome as a spring shower. At some considerable distance above me and ahead, a sharp light revealed a grey chamber with no visible decoration. As I climbed the inclined and seemingly-endless passageway, the Priests below, took up a low resonant chant. The higher I climbed, the acoustics strangely seemed to amplify the chanting, such that, by the time I arrived at the entrance, the chanting left little place in my consciousness for thought.

Breathing hard as I arrived on the threshold, I knew this was the burial chamber of the Pharaohs. In the stark grey chamber, all there was was a large stone sarcophagus and Maitreya. Rising from prayer in front of the empty sarcophagus, he came forward and offered me a blindingly white robe, identical to the one he also wore. Warm to the touch and appearing to be of the finest silk, the fabric was unlike any I had ever encountered. The room was strangely illuminated. Unlike the earlier rooms and passageways, where the light appeared to emanate from within the walls, this light appeared to originate from the very air itself. It was of a far finer frequency and felt to be revitalizing as it touched my skin. Maitreya kissed me on both cheeks before speaking.

"The time has come, Yeshua. In this chamber your heart will be pierced by the Black Light. The Mind will be no more and your thoughts will be that of the Christ. We will become Brothers in Light." He helped put the robe over my head. Although it hung like the heaviest velvet, it had no weight. It also felt as if I had attended this same ceremony before.

"Only the light of stars can penetrate the Great Pyramid and only the purest heart can bear the Flame," he spoke as though this was all not new to me. It's hard to say whether I was lead or my motions were guided by some unconscious conditioning; but I lay down in that cold and empty Sarcophagus and awaited my fate.

"Now the World will tremble at your passing. The light of a new age has dawned."

What occurred then is beyond description. I recall how my dear friend Lun would often tell me that, beyond a certain level of consciousness, the only means of communicating was through abstract symbols. At the time he had tried to explain, I hadn't been able to comprehend. Now it was obvious and my dear friend hadn't lied. Many things became known to me. I also understood that my earthly father had not been of this earth. The star system of Sirius no longer held any mysteries for me.

After that endless night, although I retained the memories of one by the name of Yeshua ben Joseph, I no longer identified with the limitations of that personality.

By the time I returned to Judaea, my cousin John's fame had spread far and wide. 'The Wild Baptist' many called him. Besides openly criticizing Herod for marrying his dead brother's wife - in no uncertain terms, John had taken to the Indian tradition of baptizing people in the Jordan. The Sanhedrin looked to have him killed, or permanently removed. John's Baptism by-passed their need for sacrifice AND the three trips to Jerusalem each year! The coffers of the Temple were being directly affected - but John was very popular with the people. Besides flouting the authority of the Men in Black, it wasn't wise to publicly humiliate Herod. It has to be admitted that Herod had done more to restore the Holy Temple than any of his Jewish predecessors, but nevertheless he wasn't a true-born Jew. If it hadn't been for his degrading willingness to prostrate himself in front of the whole Roman Senate, Herod wouldn't have assumed the Judaean throne at all. Perhaps he considered it a small price to pay for such gain.

It was something of a shock when I first saw John again. There were perhaps two hundred people crowded around the river bank. In the river, was the unmistakable figure of John, now a bear of a man. I recognized him by common description rather than memory. He had taken to wearing the skins of dead animals he had found in the caves. We had both been boys when I left for India, now we both stood at the brink of a new dawn for Israel.

"It's the Baptist from Engedi," I heard a merchant say. "Claims to speak *for* God!"

"How can the people take him seriously?" another spoke. "Just look at those skins he's wearing! No wonder he left the Engedi caves - I bet the animals threw *him* out!"

"He first appeared in the market square. - Just sat there for seven days, in total silence," the first merchant continued. "Because of his smell and the skins, no one dare ask his business. Finally, he just stood up and shouted so wildly that even the camels stood still to listen!"

"I heard. He was ranting about *another* Messiah coming. 'It is prophesied' he said - as if that were his authority. Then, before anyone could question him, he disappeared. Caused a riot, I heard."

"He's another one preaching 'The Last of Times'. It doesn't take a lot to get the people going," the first merchant concluded.

"Yet another Holy man to rub salt into the Roman heel!" the second agreed. "These crazy men should learn to live *in* the world before they go upsetting our waters!"

"But, where there's friction, there's profit," the first happily pointed out. "We supply fewer goods for higher prices. Go ahead Wild Man, baptize away!" he shouted towards the crowd below.

"Perhaps we should join them - as a gesture?" the second merchant spoke with a broad grin.

"Why not! He's good enough to provide us with a good living, the least we can do is encourage him." Laughing, the two merchants turned their tired mules towards the river below.

It saddened me to see these two. Not because they made fun of John, but because they didn't understand the Law of Retribution. One day they would learn that the quality of energy that is directed outward, is exactly the quality of energy that returns - no matter how small.

I waited until midday for the people to begin heading for the sparse shade, leaving John at the river. From conversations I had overheard on my way down to the water, I learned a lot about John. The people openly acknowledged him as a true man of God. By his own will, he had numbered his days. He had openly branded the Temple Keepers as thieves - something everyone recognized in their hearts, but no one spoke. Many had been stoned for lesser offenses, yet he still refused to modify his speech.

"I cleanse you with water," I heard him say. "This is a symbolic cleansing of Eternal Soul. A brother in blood will come and he will cleanse you with the fire of the Holy Spirit. The fan is already in his hand and he'll separate the wheat from the chaff - and you won't know him."

"How could we NOT recognize the Messiah?" the man just Baptized demanded. "Our daily lives are governed by the Laws of God! Of course we'll recognize him."

"Unless you learn to listen with your heart, his words will mingle with the dust," John calmly spoke.

"But surely we'll recognize him by his deeds?" another argued.

"The miraculous can be found in each drop of water," John said, scooping up a handful of water and letting it run between his fingers. "Yet now, who can recognize that life giving force? I tell you, this man is a King among men - a man whose shoe I am not worthy to remove." John looked around as the handful of people looked at him, dumbfounded - and offended. Less than comforted by his words, the remaining people went looking for shade and a place to picnic higher up the hillside.

"Cousin," I softly spoke. John turned and saw that it was me. Without any show of greeting, he submerged himself in the warm brown water and then stood up.

"Cousin," he answered, wiping the water from his face and looking sideways towards me. How I wanted to rush forward and hold him in my arms once more. I knew him well enough to know he also wanted the same. "There are many eyes and too few hearts," he spoke, gesturing to the populated hillside. "Has my time come?"

"It has," I answered "You have spent it well, since we last met. Then we spoke as children, now we speak as men in the sight of God. We've become men who'll cause brother to kill brother. This is the burden we've chosen to bear this lifetime."

"When we returned from Egypt, Matheno taught me so much at Engedi. He showed me death is no enemy to man. 'It's a friend who, when his work is done, cuts the cord that binds the human boat to earth' he would say." John looked down into the water as though he could see his beloved mentor in the rippled brown reflection. "- So that it can sail off to smoother seas," I continued. "It's only selfishness that makes men call back the departed. Did he speak of who you truly are?"

John hesitated before answering, as though this secret had been held so long, he was reluctant to draw it out into the light of day. "He spoke a great deal about the prophet Elijah," he finally spoke.

"And did you deny it?" I gently queried.

"I've had dreams in which there were memories. Elijah is no stranger to me."

"Then you also know where my path lies?"

"I only know that every fiber of my being has been purified so that it might carry the fire of Spirit and realize this moment," he spoke nervously. "Your way has been prepared." Placing his left palm against my forehead and his right arm under my back, he pushed me backwards beneath the water. The strange light that had been present in the Upper Chamber of the Pyramid, passed from John's palm into a region just above my eyes. Almost as a detached spectator, I watched as the ethereal fire raced though my body, burning all dross and shadow. Being submerged, the fire was contained within the confines of my physical body. I now knew my purpose!

How strange, that later that same day, I would be married in the flesh - two marriages in the one day. How many people had walked this earth and had such a curious day I wondered. Less than a few and perhaps none. The ceremonies had been brief and simple. Vows were exchanged and Mary looked radiant. Joseph figured prominently in the formalities and now leaned across the table to speak in confidence.

"You have chosen well, Nephew - both in marriage and destiny." For an instant I thought he knew about my meeting with John and then I realized, he referred to my conceding to his 'request'. "Peter you know...?"

"I knew a Peter in the shipyards - he was one of your captains?" I answered.

"That was many years ago, Yeshua. Then, he captained sailors, now he captains our forces around Galilee."

"Are they Pharisees or Zealots?" I asked, hoping to sound more interested than I really was.

"Both," he answered proudly. "For this one purpose, we've managed to get them to reconcile their differences. Admittedly they've trained separately, but they'll come together when the time's right."

"Tell me Uncle," I spoke, eating the flesh of a ripe fig and appearing to be casual. "What if I had said no?"

"I'd have to give it a lot of thought," he answered, trying to appear as though he hadn't already made plans for that eventuality.

"And I do have other brothers?" I prompted with a smile.

"It wouldn't have been easy," he conceded.

"Being the eldest and head of the family, it *wouldn't* have been easy," I spoke, toying with the remaining figs in my bowl. "And the people would only look to the eldest of the bloodline." I deliberately left my words to linger, so he would be forced to respond.

"As I said, it wouldn't have been easy," he answered, a little flustered.

"How would you have had me killed, Uncle? Would you have done it yourself?" I asked equally.

"Nephew!" he answered, outraged at such a suggestion, yet knowing that he was prepared to carry out exactly that plan.

"Come now Uncle - a man whose traveled the world's oceans and has said that he's prepared to disown his own brother's family? If such a man was prepared to lose an entire family over one nephew, wouldn't that same man see it as a small price to pay - for gaining the whole of Judaea? Our blood is the same and James would be a more acceptable figurehead for your plans?" I spoke without any trace of emotion.

"It may not have come to that," he reluctantly conceded.

"And Sunday may not follow the Sabbath?" I pointed out the inevitability of the situation.

He could see that his politicking wouldn't smooth the cracks in our relationship, so spoke directly. "Sometimes sacrifices are called for. We are God's Chosen, yet we allow our land's to be ruled by Gentiles! Surely this is God's way of making us earn our heritage," he spoke, raising his voice and showing his true motivation.

"Can a man *know* the mind of the Creator?" I coolly asked.

He prepared to answer but then sat back, thinking better of it. "You sit there so calmly eating your figs, yet your words have hidden barbs, Yeshua. Even in your youth, no one could better you in debate. I remember in the Temple..."

"Debate! You claim to know God's will in the same breath as you speak of murder!" I spoke directly, unable to remain calm any longer.

"Brother!" James suddenly spoke beside me. "You dare raise your voice to our Uncle?! Who has provided the food on our table these past years? Uncle, please forgive my brother, he's learned foreign manners and has forgotten the meaning of charity..."

"Charity?" I turned to James. "Charity is given from the heart - without thought of return. Ask your *Uncle* what he wants from me!"

I remember how embarrassed James was, as he looked around the gathering. "Speak softly! Remember, you're the groom. Is this what you learned with your Yogis: how to offend those that love you?! Maybe it would be better if you hadn't returned, Yeshua!"

"Perhaps I should leave," Joseph spoke as he stood up from the table.

"No, it's me that should apologize," I spoke, putting my hand on his arm. "James is right Uncle, foreign travel has taught me foreign manners. I ask your forgiveness." I offered an embrace to seal our understood agreement. Joseph barely nodded, recognizing that what I was offering, was a great deal more than a simple apology.

"All is forgiven. We understand each other well, Nephew. No offense is taken. Come, let's return to the festive spirit. Wine for a toast!" he called out so that everyone could hear.

Nadab, the house-servant looked nervous, avoiding Joseph's eye. In the background I could see Mother rapidly talking with the other servants. Something was wrong. I walked over to Nadab and spoke indirectly beside him.

"My mother seems concerned, Nadab?" He glanced quickly at me and then away, uncertain whether he should speak. It's true I was the head of the household, but I had been away for many years. "I ask you as a friend Nadab." He smiled warmly that I should address him on equal terms, when by rights, I could demand his response.

"The wine, Master Yeshua," he simply stated.

"What about it?" I replied.

"More guests have arrived than we had expected."

"And?"

"The wine has run out. Your Uncle's called for a toast and there isn't enough to fill everyone's glass." He hung his head in deep personal shame. In the distance, I could see my mother trying to apportion the quantity of wine that remained. Catching my eye and seeing that I was aware of the situation, Mary came over.

"Yeshu, I've shamed your father's house," she began. "I should have bought more than I thought necessary." She stood helpless, tears welling gently in her eyes.

"Didn't Nadab tell you?" I asked.

"Tell me what?" she spoke, looking to the house-servant. Nadab looked confused and helpless.

"That I brought skins from the market."

"With all the excitement of your arrival, Master Yeshua - I was confused," he diplomatically answered, yet was none the wiser. The relief on mother's face, caused her tears to become those of laughter. Quickly she hurried off to placate the waiting guests.

"Quickly," I addressed Nadab. "Take the empty skins and fill them from the well. Don't let anyone see what you're doing."

"But the toast... what...?" he started to ask.

"Do *exactly* as I say, Nadab!" I ordered.

"But the wine...?"

"Nadab, have I ever questioned your authority as keeper of my Mother's house?" I sharply spoke.

"Never, Master."

"Then I ask you to respect my wishes - and say nothing about what you might see," I spoke leaving little room for argument or debate.

Now even more confused, Nadab hurried off, certain of his coming humiliation as keeper of the household. Joseph stood largely up, in readiness to deliver the toast. His glass was filled while others waited with empty glass'.

"Where's your glass Nephew?" he asked looking pointedly at me. "The toast is to honor you. You must drink with us?" Mary, my bride, passed me her almost empty glass.

"That's a beggarly toast," Joseph pointed out. "On such an occasion?"

Seeing Nadab had returned, I held up my glass for him to see. Although very reluctant, he came forward with the wine skins and, at my prompting, began to pour. Only because I was directly facing him, could I see the look of astonishment on his face, as the red liquid poured from the skin. He allowed himself a brief look into my face before rushing off and filling the glass' of the other guests. Besides myself, it was a day Nadab wouldn't soon forget! Joseph drank from his glass.

"A fine wine to launch my brother's son into wedlock - and yet, fine enough to launch Israel into a new day," Joseph spoke addressing the crowd. "You have done well Nadab," he spoke honoring the keeper of the house. Nadab bowed graciously towards Joseph and threw the most subtle look towards me.

"The greater news is," Joseph continued "Yeshua has stopped his wanderings and has agreed to take up his position as head of the House of David." So simply put and yet so pregnant with meaning. The crowd applauded enthusiastically, yet surprised. The implication of a confrontation with the Sanhedrin wasn't lost on their ears.

"The Temple Keepers will soon look to a *true* Jewish King! Those that have been invited tonight, I've grown up with and trust with this message. It's not to be openly declared, until our hand is ready. - Perhaps I should say 'fist'?" At this, the crowd applauded even more warmly than before. "It may take one year, perhaps two - but Israel has waited long enough!"

"As Yeshua's brother, I'd like to hear this from his own lips," James spoke from a distance. "Are you prepared to give up these travels with strangers and magicians, to look after the needs of Israel?" he spoke evenly, but his distrust was evident.

"I am," I simply stated.

"Are you prepared to fight the Romans?" he goaded.

Before I could answer, Joseph interrupted.

"It wouldn't be to our advantage that Yeshua be openly declared. At least, not to the uninitiated," he spoke, making eye contact with each and every person in the courtyard. His look held an inherent threat to anyone who might consider betraying his trust.

"Yeshua will present himself as what he is - a learned Rabbi. A far-traveled Rabbi will attract an even greater following. The Sanhedrin won't be alerted to our - or rather - 'his' true purpose. To the Romans, he'll just be another wise man with many followers."

"Troy had its horse and we have our brother," James added in jest, though there was little love in his words. "Still, I'd like to hear it from Yeshua."

Sensing the crowd's expectancy, I stood up to respond. "As blood speaking to blood, I tell you, my journeys have ended. And as my good Uncle has said, a new day *is* at hand!"

Again they applauded. I looked towards James and could see he felt I hadn't answered fully. With the formalities ended, the music began and the celebrations proceeded with enthusiasm. Joseph came over and drew me aside.

"From this time forward, it would be better if my hand isn't seen," he spoke.

"You mean your 'fist', Uncle?" I joked. The corners of his lips curled in a smile, while his eyes remained impassive.

"I'll be able to help our purpose much more, than if I'm openly declared," he continued.

"But I don't know anything about politics and war," I protested. "How should I proceed?"

He pointed to the short and grizzled man I recognized from my youth. "Peter there, will be your tutor." He waved for Peter to come and join us. "He's prepared ten men who'll travel with you. They're Galilean and can be trusted."

"Yeshua, I've heard many good things about you since our years in the yards," Peter greeted. "It'll be my privilege to guide you - and perhaps learn from you."

"Thank you," I answered.

"We've waited too many years for this time and we're well prepared," he continued.

"What kind of men do you have, Peter?" I asked.

"Men hardened by the sea," he replied, reluctant to divulge any more information. "Men who would gladly lay down their lives - if ordered."

"Lets pray that good and brave men don't have to face such a choice," I spoke, aware of how closely Joseph was watching me. Joseph stroked his beard in considered thought, before speaking.

"Though you've traveled far, Yeshua, I don't think it could be said you were *of* the world," he spoke as diplomatically as he could.

"You mean I haven't known the hardship of battle?" I spoke voicing what was on his mind, though remembering the Kumbha Mehla. He appeared relieved that I understood his position.

"Exactly! Peter will deal with the more 'harsh' realities of our undertaking," he spoke, being careful to choose exactly the right words.

"'My' undertaking?" I corrected, using his own earlier correction. Again he smiled in condescension and again his eyes remained unmoved..

"There is a lot to learn Nephew," he continued, without mention of my correction. "Many Jewish bodies hang from Roman crucifixes. That's the reality of defying Roman law. The real tragedy is that most have been betrayed *by* the Men in Black. Those that should be the defenders of our faith have turned out to be our own secret executioners. Are you still prepared to continue?"

"I gave my word," I answered. He looked for further confirmation, but from my expression knew he had all I was prepared to give.

As if the day hadn't been a day of firsts, so too was the night. With the sounds of the revelers heard clear through the open window, I turned to Mary. Her hand-maidens had left and she stood by the bed wearing the finest pale blue nightshirt. A small garland of jasmine hung in her dark hair and she toyed nervously with the cord around her slim waist.

"It was many years since we played as children together and now.....," she spoke, uncertain as how to proceed.

"Your family does me great honor, that they should allow you to pass into my safe keeping," I spoke, putting a comforting hand on her shoulder.

"I knew you as a child, but now you're a man - and I still feel like a child," she blushed.

"I won't hold you to any vows you didn't willingly make, Mary." Although my words were directed from love, Mary reacted as if I had insulted her.

"I didn't speak of vows - they don't enter into this! I'm your wife, now." Walking over to a side-table, she picked up a small earthenware jug. "I've brought vegetable juice," she offered. Having been away so long, I had forgotten the practice of displaying the bloodied bedsheet on the morning after the wedding.

"I know your life has been with Holy men and that all this will take time," she quietly continued. "I am your wife - I can wait."

"It's strange," I spoke. "I have no fear of death, yet now - I feel less than a man."

"For a man whose words are said to be like desert honey," she gently laughed. "I somehow feel less than flattered, at the comparison between my worldly charms and Death..."

"Forgive me, Mary. I didn't mean..... It's just that I'm not used to..."

"And you think I am?" she teased.

"No, no, please," I stammered foolishly. "I just meant that I'm not used to talking with women..." I suddenly realized what a great lacking I had in my life.

"Who said anything about talk?" She took off the cord from around her waist and allowed the robe to fall from her shoulders. Her body reminded me of the pale marbled walls beneath the Pyramid. Her natural beauty was that of an innocent. There was none of the conscious sexuality I had seen in the Indian temple carvings. I felt as Adam must have before he became stained with guilt. Such beauty reminded me of God's love for each of us, unconditioned and without self-consciousness.   Mary slipped beneath the sheet and put out a hand for me to join her.

"I've studied the ways from the Yogis and..." I tried to reassure.

"Put away your books, Yeshua. While you were away, I often stayed with your mother. Sometimes we would have a visitor in the night. He taught us of the ways of Spirit. One thing he taught - a thing I already knew - is that my place is here, with you." She spoke as if it was something I already knew.

"Maitreya?" I asked in astonishment. Mary simply nodded.

"Leave your books outside the door. Trust your heart." As she spoke I could hear the reverberation of Maitreya in her words. "Since time began, men and women have loved without the need of guidance. Come." She pulled down the sheet beside her.

"How soft, the voice of a woman," I wondered as I lay down at her side.

"And here," she took my hand and placed it on her warm breast.

"I had no idea of the wonder, at being *only* a man," I answered.

"Tonight, be only a man, Yeshua.   Let me share your weight."

"How I wish it could be dissolved by a heavenly rain," I spoke, suddenly aware of my complete exhaustion.

"Maitreya has taught - and I know it's true - women have a wisdom beyond the reach of men," she softly spoke in my ear.   As she spoke, her hand lead mine to a place of ultimate feminine vulnerability. "Tonight the rain will fall gently on your shoulders."

That night, the pain of creation seared sharply through my body.   How wonderful the female body, capable of giving such depth of love. I had studied with so many Masters, but not until this night did I fully comprehend the fine thread that ran through all their lessons - love made manifest. Udraka's words came back to me as I lay with Mary quietly sleeping at my side.

"When you are older Yeshuaji, you'll discover Man's greatest secret - Woman!"   He had spoken with a smile at his lips, but his words were deeply meant. "In her, there is a Divine gift that draws out the nature in Man closest to God - a state of grace that we loosely call love. That's why I say, to obtain bliss, your thoughts must first be to God and then, to Woman. In the loving union of man and woman, there is a Divine Temple on which Ego can be sacrificed to reveal Universal Love."

I had heard him as a child, but now understood him as a man. Then, I had thought he claimed too much; now, I knew he had claimed too little.

That night I slept as I haven't, since being at my mother's breast.

The following day, Mary proudly displayed the sheets. At that time I felt completely vulnerable, yet somehow empowered. I sensed the ultimate truth of paradox, but hadn't yet penetrated the veil.

How wrong Joseph had been. He spoke of a 'True' King of Israel being on the throne 'soon'. He had anticipated, perhaps, months. In reality, three years passed before he was prepared to make his move. He hadn't anticipated the strength of resistance to his promotion into the inner ranks of the Sanhedrin. They had no argument with his knowledge of the Torah, or interpretation of such. Even with the weight of several of the elders on his side, there was resistance - and it required a unanimous decision for election. No one openly stated it, but it was because of his contact with the Gentiles. Because of his shipping trade, he was being discriminated against. A good Jew was expected to live within the bounds of the lands of Moses, in order to maintain the spiritual purity of the Chosen. Even within the bounds of Palestine, trade with the Romans and Greeks was tolerated by the Temple; but Joseph was actively importing Gentile culture with the Greek fondness for wine and non-Kosher foods. He of course argued that trade was a two-way street and that more spiritual morality was being exported to the unclean Gentiles and therefore, God's word reached a greater audience. The Elders paid lip-service in agreement, but secretly kept him from their elite membership.

In a sense I was relieved - the politics of power never won true hearts. In my own way, I traveled around the hills of Galilee, following where the wind blew. Invariably I came across someone from whom I could learn, or someone who needed the words that came from my lips. In a few short months, I gathered a reputation as an entertaining story-teller who should be invited to a family's table.

More often than not, whenever I approached a village, rather than have families argue over whose home I should visit, communal tables would be set up and food already prepared. Initially I felt awkward that such shows of abundance should be prompted by my visits, but I soon recognized the opportunity of inviting the poor to our tables. Sometimes, only enough places were set for the local dignitaries and myself, while others looked on. Innocently I would offer my place on the bench to a hungry onlooker, of which there was never a shortage. Rather than have their guest of honor without a seat, the local authorities soon learned to provide enough food and seating for anyone who wished to attend. This was how I first came to the attention of the Jerusalem Temple. After my time in India among the 'Untouchables', it hadn't even occurred to me. It was the goat-herder outside the hills of Pella who pointed out my situation.

I had seen him among the rocks and heard his plaintive call on the bone-whistle. I needed a drink and I also needed to get away from the crowd I had been addressing; so I climbed the hill. He smiled knowingly as I approached.

"A drink for the Bread Martyr?" he called out.

"Bread Martyr?" I inquired, sitting down on a rock. He pulled a goat towards him and placed the gourd in readiness to proceed with the milking. The animal gave me a cursory glance and continued pulling at the sparse vegetation.

"What else would I call a man prepared to die for bread?" the herder asked, looking to the people further down the hillside.

"How do you say such a thing when you don't even know me?" I asked, bemused.

"Don't know you!" he replied, as if the mere suggestion was ridiculous. "Because I herd goat's doesn't mean I'm not unique in the sight of God!" he protested.

"Forgive me," I answered. "I didn't mean to suggest..."

"I may be alone with these animals, but I do know things," he continued.

"Things?" I inquired. He simply smiled.

"Do you ever look at the stars, Rabbi?" he asked.

"Often" I replied.

"They whisper, you know" he spoke wistfully.

"And what do they say?" I asked, intrigued by this strange man whose body-odor was stronger that the animals he tended.

"They don't SAY anything!" he angrily responded, as if I questioned his sanity. "They whisper."

"And do you understand these 'whisperings'?" I cautiously ventured.

"I do," he answered, assuring himself that there was no one close to overhear. Taking the gourd from beneath the goat, he allowed the animal to scamper away. He then looked closely at me before passing the warm container. Satisfied that I was capable of understanding his words, he continued.

"A teacher will come who will die from eating bread" he furtively spoke, waving away a goat that strayed too close.

"Leaven or unleaven?" I asked in order to learn more from his answer.

"It's not important!" he angrily answered. "Why don't you listen - I said 'eating' bread."

"Will he choke on it?" I asked trying to sound amenable as I drank from the gourd.

"No, of course not," he answered, again making certain that no one else was within listening range. "He will be killed because he shares his bread with Tax collectors and Prostitutes." At this, he giggled as though sharing a childish joke with himself.

"But this isn't enough for a man to be killed," I tried to rationalize.

"For me or you, no" he seriously confided. "But for a man to whom others look for example..." He tapped the side of his nose knowingly, as if no more need be said.

"Are you saying that because a man eats contrary to the Law of the Temple..."

"Are you calling me a liar?" the herder demanded, jumping up and snatching the gourd away from my lips, causing much of it to spill on my shirt.

"You're mistaken.." I tried to explain.

"A liar AND mistaken" he angrily spoke, reaching for his heavy staff. Rather than enter into a confrontation with this deranged minder-of-goats, I turned away and made my way back down the hill. Several stones and rocks fell close by, to ensure I wouldn't return to harass the herder.

I wondered at his words. In India, madmen are looked on with respect - being regarded as having come too close to the Gods and still retaining some of their divine wisdom. How close had this herder come? It was true that several of the temples that I had spoken at, had pointed out the offense I caused, by sharing a common table with people they regarded as 'outcasts'. They even considered outcast those that were unable to pay the Temple taxes! India and the 'Hari-jans' was still too fresh in my mind to even consider barring these people that the Temple regarded as unworthy, from my table. The learned men of the Temple and society's affluent already had their reward, but these people had nothing. Most wandered the countryside in pitiful groups, looking for day-work on other people's land - even though many of them had previously been land-owners themselves. I had chosen not to see that the local priests of the towns I visited never sat at my table. Their unspoken protest of my eating habits had not gone unnoticed. Perhaps this goat-herder was the finger of God, drawing my attention to a fatal flaw in my world?

"Be certain that the tax-collectors and fallen-women will see the kingdom of God before ANY that advertise their piety through robes of Holiness and false humility," I had answered one outraged Rabbi. "Their reward is already given by the acknowledgment of society. If a person does charitable works, it should only be known by his own conscience and God." The Rabbi had agreed with my words, yet his eyes looked defensively around to his eager entourage of pupils and servants.

Several days later, I returned to Nazareth. It had been so many years since I had seen it and I needed reassurance of my past. So much had changed in recent months and I felt slightly adrift. To feel the worn stones beneath my feet and the sweet smell of the animals, my heart was eased. The still and radiating warmth of the narrow streets reminded me of the bread, fresh from the earth-baked ovens of my youth. Now I felt comfortable that the boy had become a man. Peter had come with me, so that I could be more informed about Joseph's plans. As we walked, we came across the Chief Rabbi of Nazareth and his entourage. Peter put his hand on my arm and told me to wait while he continued ahead. I took his lead, grateful to be alone for a few moments. Putting his head forward, Peter tried to pass the Rabbi unnoticed. The Rabbi recognized him and stopped in mid-conversation.

"Peter?" he called out.

Peter continued walking, apparently deep in thought.

"Peter!" the Rabbi again called. This time Peter was forced to respond.

"Rabbi Eli," he acknowledged.

"It's been more than a year since we saw you in the synagogue," the Rabbi pressed.

"I've been in Galilee working on the boats," Peter justified.

"I've also heard you keep the company of strangers?" the Rabbi prompted.

"None that didn't speak our tongue," Peter defended.

"A man from the East - claiming to be another Messiah, I've heard?"

"You speak of Yeshua of the House of Joseph?" he answered.

"The son of the Mason?" the Rabbi asked in surprise.

"The same," Peter replied. "And you know he's a true born Jew - not from the East." Peter now understood the reason the Rabbi wanted to speak to him.

"You avoid my question, Peter," the Rabbi pressed. "Does he claim to be a Messiah?"

"I haven't heard him claim that. He has traveled among the Holy men of the East though - for many years, I believe." Peter had little respect for the men who held their power as adjuncts to the Sanhedrin. However, he was wise enough not to offend the status quo, particularly at this sensitive time.

"Then tell Yeshua, that the Keeper of the Scrolls will expect him to present his teaching in the Temple at - shall we say - noon tomorrow?" The words were a statement rather than a request. I stood forward to answer this arrogance immediately. Peter threw me a look that made it clear that that wouldn't be in accordance with Joseph's wishes. I reluctantly held back. I remember Rabbi Eli well from my youth and his opinions sounded as entrenched as they ever

had.   I also wondered how much support he had provided the
Essenes when they were being attacked by bandits while I was away.
"Yes, midday tomorrow we'll all have the benefit of this wise
man's teachings." The High Priest gestured to his entourage that, in
his magnanimity, they too could share what was not his to give!
With a wave of his robed arm, Peter was dismissed and the entourage
proceeded like chickens down the road.
The remains of our Essene community weren't hard to find.
Several of the buildings had been burned to the ground.   The few
buildings that remained, were in a poor state of repair and contained
braying asses and livestock.   I felt the pain of lost youth as I watched
another homesteader remove stones from what had been our
communal dinning room and use them in his own new construction.
There was no evidence of other homes being vandalized and I
wondered at the story Hor had told me. The local priests had always
been welcome in our community - but it was incredulous that *only*
our buildings had been attacked?
The following day, I went to the market square.   I naturally
gravitated to the animal quarter and began talking with some camel
traders that had recently arrived from the East. They cooked tea over
the small communal fire, in the manner of the Indians. Milk and
spices were added to the pot and immediately my memories of India
lived again.   They were spice traders and had recently bought
Frankincense from the fabled Ubar, by the Arabian gulf.   Such
spices were expensive in Judaea and it wasn't always wise to speak so
openly of what you carried. There were many bandits along the trade
routes and many unclaimed bones bleaching beneath the fierce sun.
I always found the desert people to be among the happiest.   In many
ways I envied their lifestyle - wandering among the shifting sands
and never held to a single place.   They loved to tell simple jokes.
Many I'd heard on my travels along the Silk Route. They had
evidently heard them many times before as well, yet there was a joy
in the ritual of retelling, a joy that only children have.
One of the drovers carried with him a small monkey, which he
treated as his own child.   The animal had learned a comic routine
and was always the center of attention. He loved performing. We
all typically gravitated into a tight-nit circle to hear the jokes, but

then, at his master's signal, the ape picked up a small stick and systematically beat back the audience - so that the ape would have a circular arena in which to perform. Then, walking slowly around the inner perimeter of the audience, the monkey threw back his head and disdainfully looked away. Prompted by his owner, the audience then pleaded with the ape to perform his 'world renown' tricks. It took the giving of a small sweet banana from a member of the audience for the ape to relent. It was in the middle of these antics and laughter, that I saw Rabbi Eli and his entourage approach. It was apparent that he didn't recognize me, but had obtained my description, since he came straight towards our group.

"Master Yeshua, the council humbly requests to know why you haven't presented proof of your calling at the synagogue?" he spoke, barely pausing to take breath.

"Humbly request?" I answered. "I understood it to be an order."

"No I don't think so," the Rabbi responded, aware I wasn't going to be brow-beaten by rank or bluster. The camel drovers had little time for Rabbis and still less for those that disturbed their entertainment. Some stood up, preparing to physically remove the Rabbi from the ape's arena. I put up a hand to forestall their action. Realizing that the ape took precedence in this place, the Chief Rabbi waved back his entourage.

"I'm not called by your ministry," I quietly stated, hoping to save the Rabbi any further humiliation.

"You have a ministry higher than that of the Keeper of the Scrolls?!" the Rabbi suddenly turned. "Then, you should indeed address us of your calling." His tone held no indication of wanting to learn, but rather to condemn.

"Rabbi, your place is in the synagogue," I answered, not wishing to pursue this line of conversation.

"You don't intend to answer the charges of claiming to be a Messiah?" he sarcastically demanded for the benefit of his own following.

"Rabbi, you arrive here and ask that I might address the synagogue - so that you can learn. Now you speak about 'charges'? What would be the point - since you don't even know your own mind, yet you wish to know mine?" At this, the Rabbi's face flushed red with rage. His followers edged slightly away, the Rabbi's anger being something they evidently didn't want to be on the receiving end of.

"You presume to lecture *me* - the Keeper of the Scrolls?!" he spoke in disbelief.

"I presume nothing," I sharply answered. "Who gave you the right to question me? My proof is in my words and deeds. If you want proof, you're welcome to follow me."

"Follow you.....follow *you*!" he stammered, almost choking on his own words.

The Arabs laughed openly at his pomposity. Affronted, he turned away at a loss for words and stormed out of the market square.

"Without humility there can be no true understanding." Hor's words echoed in my head.

Days later, I found myself walking along a dusty road with Peter and a handful of his chosen men. It had been decided that they appear to be my disciples and so I tried, in part, to explain this teaching of the Heart. On the outskirts of a small village we saw the ragged outline of a leper moving unevenly towards us. A pack of roving dogs snapped close to his heals, but his large stick kept them at bay. Seeing us, he moved deliberately in our direction. All lepers knew, by power of the Temple, that they were to leave the road at a distance of no less than seven feet; if others were making use of that same path. So, by moving towards us, he was taking a deliberate action to break the law. His skin was hideously bleached and a rough cloth covered his flaking face. Peter moved forward and prepared to use his sword. The man held his ground and called ahead to us.

"I've heard you have a wise man, a man who knows something about healing?" he called. "If there is any truth in the rumor, let me be healed." The man appeared to be making a demand rather than an appeal which, given his situation, was very strange. He evidently held his own life so cheap that he could afford to be belligerent with it.

"If you don't leave the road, this will save you the concern of any healing," Peter called back as he showed his sword.

"Peter!" I shouted. "Hold your blade and *never* come between me and my Father!" Amazed and surprised that I should speak so loudly against him, Peter stood aside for me to pass. The man fell to his knees as I approached. I reached forward and helped him back onto his feet.

"Your faith is your savior," I quietly spoke. The man had the most piercing blue eyes I had ever seen and, instead of the usual odor of decaying flesh that the lepers had, I smelled the faintest trace of Jasmine. There appeared to be a spark of recognition in his face, yet I was certain we had never met before. He began suddenly moving about as though trying on new clothes. His body moved more easily that it had previously. He grinned broadly at my friends, as they doubtfully approached.

"Now go - and tell no one," I ordered, aware of how easily people exaggerated in their story-telling!

With an uncharacteristic flourish, the man left the road as he had previously been ordered and, with a generous gesture of his arm, offered us the free road. This gesture was evidently meant for Peter and his cohorts. Although not fully cured, the leper seemed satisfied with the difference. In other men there would have been gratitude. From this man, there was an unsettling presumption towards my friends.

As we traveled on, Mark came alongside to speak with me.

"I'm interested to hear what your Eastern teachers would have said about that man, Yeshua?"

"In what respect?" I inquired, since Mark had never before shown undue interest in matters of the spirit.

"Does he have leprosy because of something he did in a previous life, or is it something his parents have done?"

"A good question," I reflected. "Karma does work in the way you suggest. However, I believe that sometimes these things are put in our path to show us the wonders of God's mercy."

That night we slept on a hill above the town. How clear the sky, with its infinite number of stars. I loved to smell the fragrant grasses before drifting into sleep.

We carried little food with us and so I looked forward to the fresh-baked bread and olives, ahead in the town. However, before we could enter the town, we were met by a delegation - who politely but firmly, lead us directly to the Synagogue.

"What's happening?" Peter asked mistrustfully as we were being bustled forward.

"I've no idea," I replied. Among the people guiding us towards the temple, I recognized one of the entourage of Rabbi Eli from Nazareth. His eyes deliberately avoided mine.

"Breakfast may be delayed," I joked to alleviate the look of concern on several of our group's faces.

In the temple, the Rabbis were all in full regalia and it appeared as if a religious court was in session. We were ushered forward, where I could see the leper we had met the day before. He appeared to have fully recovered from his affliction. It also appeared that he had been the focus of questioning before our arrival. The court remained silent as we were ushered forward without explanation. Out of the corner of my eye I saw a man conspicuously seated and in the grip of some mental affliction. I studiously avoided looking in his direction.

"Rabbi," the head Rabbi spoke casually, as though voicing a thought that had just occurred to him. "Which is the greatest of the commandments?"

I slowly looked around, recognizing this for the theological trap it was intended to be. Again, I avoided looking towards the man with the mental affliction. He nervously giggled behind his hand, like a child about to perform some magic trick.

"Which is the greatest commandment? I recognize no greatest," I quietly spoke so that he was forced to lean forward to hear me.

"No greatest?" he responded, unimpressed with my reply.

"I see them all as one, joined by a silken thread of gold, which is Love."

"Very good, very good," he answered, as if I had cleverly avoided falling into some concealed trap. The audience looked expectantly towards him, waiting for his next thrusting question.

Taking some moments for theatrical effect, he again spoke as if another thought had just occurred to him. "Rabbi, we've been taught it's sinful to work on the Sabbath? Yet today, as you traveled this way, your men pulled ears of corn from the fields?"

Peter had had quite enough of this 'civil' questioning and stood forward. "We've traveled a long way to be here and we were hungry!" He turned to face the hostile crowd, fingering the hilt of his sword in suggestion that he was quite prepared to take the argument further.

"The Sabbath was made for man - not man for the Sabbath," I responded. "This custom was made to keep an ordered society, not to bring man closer to his creator." The man I had seen previously at the camel market stood forward.

"Do you presume to know more than the Sanhedrin?" he asked with contempt thinly disguised in his voice.

"I presume nothing," I answered. "And I claim nothing. I am the son of my Father."

The crowd restlessly moved and grumbled, uncertain as how to interpret my words. Was I referring to my bloodline, or was I claiming to be the direct son of God? How badly they wanted to ask directly, but were afraid. How sad that a place of God should know fear, when trying to ascertain truth. The real question they dared not ask was: *'Yeshua ben Joseph, do you openly blaspheme by claiming to be the Son of God? Do you, Yeshua ben Joseph understand that by claiming such, you are calling on your own death penalty'?* I fully understood and inwardly trembled that they might be so brave as to ask. I would have to be truthful - and for that I trembled. With an almost unseen gesture, I noticed the Rabbi signal to the man with the mental affliction.

"What do you want with us, Yeshua?" the afflicted man spoke, between suppressed spasms of laughter. "I know you, you're the Holy one of God."

This was their trap!? Far from subtle, they expected me deliver my own statement of guilt - as they saw it. The audience fell silent in expectation. Without answering the man directly, I turned to the head Rabbi.

"Tell me Rabbi, which is lawful on the Sabbath: to do good or to do evil? To save life or kill?" The Rabbi shrank from the responsibility of answering such a question. Such cowardice! Their words held no love, only hypocrisy. To do good was God's will, yet to contravene it by taking action on the Sabbath showed the division between God's will and that of man's 'apparent' sacred law.

"You men care more for the letter of the Law that the spirit for which it was formed! You're like the Pharisees and their politics of Holiness. By tithing everything down to a single grain of salt, they are devoutly 'Holy' - but neglect Justice and Love! What they intend to be pure, they are defiling in the eyes of God! Have you so easily forgotten General Pompey? He was wiser than many a Rabbi!" I looked around and saw that the people hadn't understood my words. "Was it one hundred years ago, or one thousand - it might as well be the same!"

"Ninety three," Mark offered, understanding precisely what I was trying to convey.

"He knew our slavish adherence to the word," I explained. "He attacked Jerusalem on the Sabbath and no Jew resisted! The following day, twelve thousand of our brothers rose up - and were slaughtered. The Sabbath was created for man, not man for the Sabbath!"

The Priests were not used to being confronted with Greek logic in matters of Law and I sensed, rather than saw, Peter's men prepare to defend themselves. The man with the mental illness laughed loudly, sensing the open hostility. I could take it no more, so turned to him and shouted.

"Be quiet and get out of him now!"

The man let out a horrible scream and fell writhing to the floor. Cowering away from me, his eyes made direct contact with mine for the first time.

"I order you to leave him, now!" The onlookers shrank back from him - as if they could be contaminated by what they considered this 'Devil's work'. After deliberately and violently banging the side of his head against the cold stone floor, he suddenly stopped - as if he had woken from a dream. Then, quietly, he gathered himself together and made his way apologetically back through the parting crowd. Although deeply embarrassed, the madness had left his eyes. The Ushers of the Synagogue prepared to remove the people, so that they shouldn't witness further blasphemy. Rather than have the people removed, I pushed my way towards the door. With his back close towards me, Peter drew his sword and stopped anyone from attempting to restrain me. The people looked to the head Rabbi for a response to this show of arms.

"Have a care, Yeshua ben Joseph, because you won't be welcome here again," he called above their heads. "They'll be told about this in Jerusalem!" This was no empty threat, yet somehow I felt relieved. It was as if I had thrown a lifeline out from the restriction of Joseph's protected boat.

After a little more than a day's journey, we found ourselves in the hills to the south of Galilee. Peter pointed ahead.

"Just beyond this ridge, we have nearly three hundred of our finest men," he spoke with evident pride. "They represent the main body of our force."

"Only three hundred?" I asked.

"For surgery, only one small and sharp knife is required and we have the sharpest of knives - the Iscarii."

"You're prepared to work with the Iscarii?" I asked somewhat surprised.

"They're the best men with knives and they have experience. The Romans will feel their tickle between the shoulders."

"Assassins?" I asked.

"It's true some of their leaders have trained with the Assassins, but we have no murderers here," he answered defensively.

"Even in India they've heard of the Iscarii," I spoke, trying to hide my disdain. "They cloak themselves in darkness and kill in silence?"

"There's more rumor than truth about them," Peter defended. "What I can say is, their methods of weakening large and powerful armies, is without equal. We are few and the Romans are many."

"How have you managed to coordinate all the different groups?" I inquired, to divert the conversation away from the sensitive issue of paid killers working under Peter's command. "For generations the tribes have been at each other's throats?"

"They've finally understood, that only by coming together, do we have any hope of getting rid of the Romans," Peter responded with a clear sense of personal responsibility and pride.

"But differences of blood can't be overcome by simple agreement?" I pressed.   "One spark of trouble could send the whole thing up in flames?"

"Obviously there's friction, but we've appointed leaders of each group who've accepted *personal* responsibility for their own men," Peter cautiously stated.   "So far, it's worked."

As we came to the crest of the ridge, there below was the encampment.

"Here is the fist that will drive the might of Rome from our lands," Mark now spoke beside me.

"But so few?" I asked.

"When we move towards Jerusalem, others will join us," Peter again spoke - deliberately not revealing just how many 'others' would be joining us.   Since the incident in the Synagogue, Peter had become more cautious as to what he told me.   I don't think that it was a lack of trust, so much as the fact he realized I wasn't going to be a mere puppet for Joseph.   It was as though I was only being told, what was necessary for my part in the grand scheme.

Below us, men drilled in close-quarter fighting and the use of rudimentary siege weapons.

"The Romans attack in a Phalanx," the lead instructor shouted, so that all could hear.   "They form a square that holds it's shields above and around itself.   It's like attacking a turtle, the shields simply deflect any arrows. Force cannot be met with force, we have to guide it."

"One of our best instructors," Peter spoke beside me.   "He served as a slave to one of the Roman Consuls, actually in Rome. He was able to see at first hand, how they defeated their enemies in Gaul."

"The intention of the armored Phalanx is to drive a wedge down the middle of the opposing army," the instructor continued. "Remember our father Moses - part like the Red Sea.   We must learn to yield like water and then snap at their heels!   Become like a cloud of insects and chase the Roman cattle into the sea."

Suddenly, serious fighting broke out on the periphery of the encampment.   The instructor broke off from his talk and waved a handful of chosen men to break up the disturbance. Peter stepped forward and the instructor immediately deferred to him.

"Bring those men here," he commanded without hesitation.

An old and younger man were roughly brought forward. The younger man bled from a deep cut in his arm. The instructor went forward and briefly questioned the men. He then turned to inform Peter and looked uneasily towards me, a stranger in their camp.

"These two have flocks of sheep", he spoke. "This one married the daughter of the other and, as is the custom, he gave half his flock to his father-in-law."

"He gave diseased sheep - this is how he treats a father!" the older man shouted out so everyone could hear.

"The father says he gave sheep, knowing they had the sleeping sickness," the instructor spoke, shooting a look to the older man. The man cowered from the instructor's authority.

"Is this true?" Peter asked the younger man.

"No!" the man emphatically replied.

"His animals infected my whole flock and now I have nothing," the older man spoke, unable to restrain his anger. The instructor moved closer so that his face should be intimidatingly close to the older man's, but he continued. "I'm an old man, but God has left me enough strength to avenge this injustice."

"What do you say?" Peter addressed the younger man.

"He lies. He knew his were already infected - ask his daughter." The man spoke looking around for his wife to verify the truth. "I even gave more than was the custom, to cover his expected losses."

"He's a liar - he's a liar before God!" the old man screamed at the top of his voice. "And what son of Israel would dare call his father a liar!" At this, both families pressed forward behind each man, prepared for a bloody confrontation.

"Enough!" Peter shouted, seeing that things could easily get out of control. "It'll be decided in the circle. Since they are of the same family by marriage, the father will be represented, but I ask for the leader of another group to come forward and represent the son?"

None of the other leaders regarded this as their fight, so no one stepped forward. In fairness to the other leaders, they represented their own families, so why should they risk dying for this man.

"As God is their witness, both men will be branded outcasts?" Peter pleaded.

Still there was silence. Then, the people at the front of the circle parted and a man with the darkest eyes I had ever seen, stepped forward. An old scar ran down from his eye to just above his jawline.

"As leader of the Iscarii, I'll act as God's witness," the man softly spoke. The defender of the old man that he would have to face, was considerably more powerful than the Iscarii. The volunteer's own group attempted to pull him back into the crowd, but he wouldn't be dissuaded.

The gathering formed a large circle, with each man linking his arms with the man at his side, so that the circle was contained. The chief instructor stepped forward and, using a length of rope, tied each of the combatants left wrists. Leaving a short length between the men ensured that each wouldn't be able to escape beyond the other's reach. The Iscarii was given his favored knife, while the other called for a short Roman sword. Each man was shown the other's weapon and formally agreed to continue.

"A present given me by dead Romans who have traveled before you Iscarii," the larger man spoke, showing the sword to the crowd. "And the way is well trod."

Circling, each man took up the slack in the rope, testing the strength of the other. The larger man made the first thrusting attack and the Iscarii only just managed to deflect it past his face. They continued circling with both blades pressed together, neither daring to part and give the other the opportunity of a first strike. Without any doubt, the larger man was the stronger and it appeared inevitable that he would be victorious. After much testing with their blades, the larger man suddenly used all his strength and pulled the Iscarii toward him. The Iscarii was pulled clear off his feet and fell past the larger man and on his back, close to the edge of the circle. In the process, his knife was hurled beyond him and into the crowd. The larger man smiled and lunged after him to deliver the death blow.

The Iscarii rolled aside, the blade barely missing him and striking a rock at his side. Moving almost as fast as the eye could see, the Iscarii looped the rope around the larger man's throat. Then, using his feet, the Iscarii kept the sword away from his exposed body as he tightened the cord around the other man's neck. Tightening with all his strength, the Iscarii forced the larger man to drop his sword.

"Mercy, mercy," the larger man barely gasped. The Iscarii looked to the crowd, who evidently believed it was God's judgment that the man should die. The Iscarii reached for the short sword and, raising it above his head, cut the rope. Released, the larger man fell choking forward to the ground. Standing up to face Peter, the Iscarii threw the sword to the ground and walked away.

The defeated and now humiliated leader, quickly retrieved his sword and moved to attack the Iscarii from behind. Seeing the crowd's horrified reaction, the Iscarii quickly turned around. Confronting him, was his fellow combatant, with his sword raised above his head in readiness to split the Iscarii's skull. Then, each man stood motionless, before the larger man slowly fell to the side, an arrow buried deep in the side of his neck. One of the fighter's own men lowered a now-empty bow, before speaking.

"My cousin's cowardice will not stain Israel's cause." The Iscarii bowed his head in gratitude to the bowman. My attention was immediately drawn to a hooded horseman who looked down from the ridge above - it was Maitreya!

"God's will has been shown," Peter addressed the crowd. "The old man knew his flock were diseased." Then he turned and directly addressed the father. "Leave these good men of Israel and seek shelter among the Gentiles. Your name will not be spoken again among the tribes of Israel."

"He lies, he lies!" the father screamed, pointing towards his son-in-law. "The Iscarii threw powder in his face. It wasn't a true test!"

Everyone present formally turned their backs on the man. He continued pleading, but was even rejected by his own family and soon left. I looked back up the hill, but Maitreya was gone!

Peter gave a few quiet orders to the chief instructor and explained who I was, before the camp returned to it's drill and training. Peter went off to speak to the iron-smith, so I continued walking with Mark.

"Men speak so easily of their love of God, but it's rare to see a man such as this Iscarii, actually put his life in God's hands," I spoke as we walked. "What do you know about him?"

"A mysterious character really, very quiet," Mark answered, greeting old friends along the way. "In his youth he witnessed the massacre of an entire Zealot village, where every last person was crucified. The scar was given to him as a reminder by the Romans. People tend to talk more about a scarred child than they do about an entire massacre."

"He's the leader of these 'knifemen'?" I asked.

"Has been for the past few years. You might have a lot in common - he spent eight years living in the Monasteries around Sinai." Mark smiled, but had little real interest in these matters. Ahead I could see the Iscarii seated on a rock and wrapping bandages around his chest, where he had received several cuts.

"Yeshua ben Joseph," Mark introduced. "This is Judas Iscarii." The man looked up and we both had recognition, yet had never met before. In my heart I felt happy, knowing that this man would in some way be a lifelong friend. He also felt an inner connection, but never spoke about it.

"I've heard of the name Yeshua - the Rabbi who travels in far countries," he warmly greeted. "Have you come to minister to our army - such as it is?"

"Yeshua is Peter's man," Mark simply explained. Having his own intelligence sources, Judas dubiously nodded his head as though considerably more had been implied by Mark's words.

"Then the Caesar's had better look to their laurels, before we take them," Judas lightly joked.

"Since you have a lot in common - with your travels in the Sinai, perhaps you could help Yeshua?" Mark offered.

"It'd be an honor for the house of Iscarii to help you Rabbi, in any way I can," he spoke from the heart.

"In a world that's strange to me, I'd be grateful for a man whose actions speak truth."

"Truth is an animal with two heads, Yeshua," Judas spoke with a smile. "Perhaps you're the wise man that can tell me if it comes or goes?"

"A man wiser than myself told me: 'a man who claims truth, at the same time declares himself a liar'," I spoke half in jest. Judas smiled and again I was struck by the darkness of his eyes. Other men with dark eyes had a glisten from the brightness of the skies. Hardly any light reflected from Judas' eyes.

"I'll leave you with Judas for the while," Mark spoke as he turned away. "Peter's holding a meeting of the leaders and I should attend." For a few moments Judas and I remained in silence, each wondering at the familiarity between us.

"I've heard that you're able to heal?" he spoke, tightening the bandages and wincing as he did.

"I have been God's instrument," I admitted.

"Are you able to teach it?" he asked.

"Do you want to learn?" I asked, looking around at the instruments of war that surrounded us.

"This isn't my choosing," he answered looking down at his bandaged body.

"Yet you lead the Iscarii?" I questioned without recrimination.

Judas was about to give a brief and proven answer and then realized in wouldn't have been adequate, so stopped for a few moments to consider.

"As a child, I witnessed hell right in front of my eyes," he began. "My brothers and sisters were mutilated, as my relatives were all being crucified. I also received a small token," he pointed to the scar running down from his eye. "For eight years I didn't speak - not a single word. I felt guilty that I suffered so little while the others...."

I put my hand on his shoulder so that he should be comforted and not feel the need to continue. He waved away my concern.

"No, it's all right," he continued. "For any other man I have a brief reply, but for you - I sense you're not like other men. I can see by the way Mark and Peter talk to you. I did try to lose myself in the Sinai monasteries by doing severe penance, but my soul found no peace. I realized God had saved me for some specific purpose - not, to be a monk. I returned to the world and found the Romans were still crucifying our people. That's why I studied the ways of war - not my choosing, my calling."

"Yet you still seem to carry a mountain of guilt?" I ventured. From any other man, I sensed Judas would have taken exception to my observation.

"Perhaps I'm wrong about my calling and my path leads in another direction?" he questioned as he stood up to adjust his clothes. "And you Rabbi, have you found your calling?"

"I too, am not here by choice," I answered. He stopped a moment to consider me and then began walking.

"I'm happy that you should add to our numbers, Yeshua, but do you bring more than words?" he questioned with some doubt in my contribution to the cause.

"In what sense?" I asked.

"I mean no offense, but how do you differ from the Temple leaders and their 'worthy' speeches?"

"How would you have me different?" I asked with a smile.

"The Sanhedrin talk of high principles, yet they allow their own people to be humiliated by the Romans. Worse still, they support Roman rule. Are you any different, do you also say we should look up to their appointed King - or Tetrarch?"

"You speak of personal humiliation, or national?" I asked.

"They're one and the same, if we *are* truly the Chosen People," he answered, satisfied that I had no more to offer than the Sanhedrin.

"The way you speak would suggest a personal humiliation?" I suggested from his response. He paused to look more closely at me.

"Okay, since you ask. On my way here from Shechem, I was forced to carry a soldier's load. Should I have said no and defied Roman rule - it wasn't my load?" he asked with defiance in his eyes.

"Why should you carry his load?" I asked

"You really don't know?" he asked in amazement.

"No, I don't."

"Then you've been away from this land too long," he spoke picking up his sword and bundle.

"Please explain. I really don't understand." Judas looked closely to confirm I truly didn't understand.

"Yeshua, it's the law of Judaea, that any Roman soldier can commandeer any non-Roman to carry his load for one mile. To refuse, is to face the full weight of the Law, as sanctioned by the Sanhedrin." He watched my reaction and smiled to himself. "So how do you differ from the Sanhedrin - do you support their Law?" I thought carefully before replying.

"If you're ordered to carry it one mile, I say you should carry it two! Show that your spirit is stronger than their rule," I answered. Judas was astonished at my reply.

"Your words are very strange for a Rabbi," he spoke, intrigued. "And if after two miles, the Roman strikes me for cheek - what should I do then?"

"Strike you - how?" I asked. Judas seemed confused and stumbled for an answer.

"In the usual way," he simply stated.

"And that is? Show me!" Judas hesitantly raised his left hand and prepared to slap me across my right cheek. I put up a hand to stop his strike. "Why the left hand?" I pointedly asked.

"Because that's what's socially acceptable," he answered, still confused.

"Acceptable?" I questioned dubiously.

"It isn't meant to hurt, simply humiliate," he answered.

"Because the left hand is 'unclean'," I explained. "It's used for bodily functions and the strike is symbolic - meant to degrade."

"So what are you suggesting?" he asked, further intrigued.

"If a man strikes you on the right cheek, offer him your left as well."

"But that would be defiance - he would have to use his more powerful right hand?"

"It would be more honest," I explained. "It would force him to accept that you're an equal in the sight of God."

"- Since you had obeyed the Law, above and beyond it's rule...?"

"If the soldier strikes you again, he would be in defiance of the law - and the Sanhedrin would be forced to rule against the Roman." Judas put his fingers against his forehead as he began to understand the implications of my words.

"I apologize, Yeshua," he quietly spoke. "To mention your calling in the same breath as the Sanhedrin, is to say that day is similar to night. You may only bring words to our cause, but each of your words, cuts deeper than ten swords."

"In India I heard of a man who offered his own leg to a man-eating Tiger. The Tiger was twice the size of the largest man and was known to have killed many men. One day, as the man was preparing his nets for fishing, the Tiger attacked. Since he was on the beach, the man had nowhere to escape, so dived under the hull of his small boat. The Tiger paced around the hidden man and then began to dig with his huge paws. It was obvious that the Tiger would soon be able to claw the man and pull him out from cover, like a clam from its shell."

"So what did he do?" Judas asked.

"He stuck out his foot, which the Tiger immediately seized. Once the man felt his foot was entirely in the Tiger's mouth, he reached out and grabbed the head of the Tiger, pulling it with all his strength. The Tiger tried to pull away but the man held on, pushing his severed leg deeper into the animal's throat. The great beast was unable to draw breath and finally suffocated - the man lived."

"Rabbi Yeshua," Judas spoke, impressed. "You understand more about battle strategy than most of the men here. If a man tries to throw you off a cliff, allow him to pull you to the edge and then, add a little of your own energy, helping him on his way. Allow him to throw himself over?"

"You understand me well Judas."

"If only you had been in the Sinai," Judas kindly offered. "I might not have had to waste so many years. Your mold is not like any Sanhedrin."

"I take that as a compliment, Judas Iscarii," I replied. Judas looked seriously at me.

"I'm not given to compliments, but I recognize a leader of men when I see one and I'd consider it a great honor, if you'd look on me as a friend."

"Friendship is the recognition Self in others," I spoke the words I had heard along the Silk Route.

"I've heard that too," Judas acknowledged. As we spoke, I felt a deep kinship and inwardly recognized that this man would in some way, assist me in achieving whatever destiny I faced. "Come," he invited. "Let's hear what Peter has planned for our future."

The entire encampment gathered around Peter and his Captains. When everyone was assembled, Peter climbed a large rock so that he could be seen and heard by everyone.

"Friends, the time has come!" he began. "We've all put aside our individual differences for the greater good of Israel. The time of waiting is over! Tomorrow we head South, towards Jerusalem."

"Will we openly confront the Romans?" a voice called from the crowd. Others echoed this thought. Peter hadn't wanted to be quite so forthright in his pronouncement, but looking towards Mark and the others, he saw little point in delay.

"Not at first," he answered. "There are too few of us. First we must be seen to control the Temple. The people won't rise up, unless they're ordered by the Temple."

"How will we do that?" the first voice called out. "None of us want blood spilled in anger on Temple grounds."

Peter put up his hands to quell the growing rumble of dissension. "No blood will be spilt - if our plan succeeds!" Peter indicated for me to join him on the rock.

"The people will only look to a person who has the Spiritual right to address them," he continued as I climbed up. "Herod only rules through might and Roman steel. The Sanhedrin only rule because they're elected from the ruling families *and* sanctioned by Herod." He let the meaning of his words fully register before continuing. "At the heart of the Sanhedrin, we have a benefactor." At this statement, there was shocked silence. "This is how we know the time is right."

"What Sanhedrin would dare speak for us?" one man voiced the thoughts of the crowd. Peter merely smiled, recognizing that he had everyone's undivided attention.

"It wouldn't be wise to say his name at this time," he cautiously responded. "If he was known inside the Temple ranks, our cause would be lost. Our primary purpose, is to remove Roman rule. Our secondary purpose...," he spoke, pausing for effect. "Our secondary purpose is to once again, have a true Jew sitting on the Judaean throne." At this, an enormous cheering broke out, as though a first-born child had been shown to be a boy and no one had any previous knowledge of the pregnancy. Looking around at the happy faces, I suddenly felt the weight of my responsibility. Peter reached for my hand and pulled me to his side.

"Here is the first-born son of the House of Joseph," he proudly announced. "Once more the blood of David will direct the hearts of Israel." Peter stepped back so that I could address the crowd. I surveyed the faces and saw the hope in their eyes and felt the need in their hearts.

"People of Israel," I began. "A day such as our forefathers dreamed, is at hand." Again a great cheer went up. "I know little or nothing about the ways of war, but I have Peter here to guide me." Another cheer of approval rose up from those who had direct dealings with Peter. He acknowledged their approval and indicated that they should listen closely to what I had to say. "You have heard it said that you should love your neighbor, but I tell you, that's easy - you should love your enemy!" Immediately the sea of faces looked to each other in blank confusion. James and Mark looked alarmed at my words. Peter stepped forward to recover the situation.

"But that's after our enemy has returned to Rome," he spoke as if we had rehearsed this joke. Several people hesitantly laughed and relief spread among the rest. Simon moved to climb the rock, intending to help me down, whether I wanted to or not. Peter and my eyes met and I knew I had already said too much. Saving Simon the effort, I climbed down.

"Those are strange words for a leader who's about to take us against the might of Rome?" Simon queried.

"We each come from different villages, but cross the river on the same boat," I answered.

"Strange words," Mark commented, apparently offended by my address to the crowd.

"Perhaps," I answered. "What these men need to know is that what matters, is in their hearts. Where there's hatred, no fruit will grow."

"You are naive, Yeshua," Mark abruptly stated. "There are many here who've had their children torn from their arms. Those children now breath galley air and pull to the rhythm of Roman drums."

"Perhaps I am naive as you say, but one thing is certain. The actions we're about to undertake, must be directed by our love of God - not hatred of the Romans."

"Are you so certain?" Peter now spoke angrily beside me. "So many of our people have been crucified for so little. Were they so wrong?"

"Doubt is our greatest enemy, Peter," I answered. "Keep faith in your heart. Didn't Moses promise this land?"

"Moses doesn't need help from me," Judas spoke bluntly, breaking into our conversation. "The love of my butchered family bring me here!"

"Roman soldiers used the necks of my family to sharpen their swords!" Thomas spoke and then spat on the ground. "And now they demand I pay their taxes! Should I love them for that, Yeshua?"

"With hatred, there will be no end to the cycle," I tried to explain, but there were no ears prepared to listen.

"Everyone has lost land and family," Peter intervened to arrest the conversation. "And now, after three years of hard training, the time has come. The Romans are about to hear a sound that'll drive them from our shores and curse the day they ever set foot here."

"And all you need do Yeshua, is play the part of a King," Mark spoke with little love in his words.

"In the coming days, our deeds will enter into the history of our peoples," Peter spoke. "And the name of Yeshua will be spoken in the Temple with pride."

A few days later, Peter suggested we take a boat out onto the sea. "It's easier to think and talk with water all around," he explained. "And no curious ears." Judas and Mark manned the boat while Peter and I talked. Galilee at that time of year was as beautiful as any place I had ever seen. White daubed houses settled by the water's edge and the grape vines were heavy with fruit.

"Your Uncle was pleased with your reception the other day," he casually spoke. Since I knew Joseph was in Jerusalem, several days away, I realized how organized they must be, for reports to travel so quickly.

"And are you my keeper?" I questioned.

"Intelligence, in a land under siege, is essential," he rightly pointed out. "And I'm my own man Yeshua. I don't dance to any man's drum!"

"I beg your forgiveness Peter. I know you are a true son of Israel," I acknowledged. "I also realize that Joseph may be the man most responsible for returning Israel to her people. It's hard for me to walk this path - my every move being judged and reported."

"His path is harder - appearing to be a loyal Sanhedrin, yet supplying funds and information," Peter pointed out. "If his real purpose was known, he'd immediately be put to death. All you need to do, is follow our cue."

"It seems I ask too much," I acquiesced. "I meant no offense to you, or Joseph."

"I understand how difficult this must be for you Yeshua, but I assure you, Joseph only has the highest good in mind."

"I don't doubt Joseph's intentions," I conceded. "It's just that all the years I've been away from this land, I've studied the ways of Love - not war. Now, I find my hands bound and I'm at the head of an army! An army who, if their demands aren't met, will follow a course of violence." Peter rubbed his face as he looked out across the waves.

"I understand your dilemma. What you have to ask yourself is: 'is the greater good served by compromising the lesser'?" For Peter this may have been a difficult question. For me, it was obvious. Good can never be quantified. The lesser, as he saw it, was no less important than the greater. To serve one is to serve all.

"If a mother wolf found that a cub had strayed from the den, would she stay with the remaining cubs to keep them safe, or go in search of the single cub?" I asked.

"You'd compare Joseph to a wild animal?!" he asked in disgust.

"The principle is the same" I answered.

"Principles are luxuries of peacetime, Yeshua. Principles have bled our people dry." His cold words were delivered almost as a challenge for me to dare contradict.

"I'll be your figurehead Peter, but there are times when I must speak what's in my heart!"

"I understand," he spoke thoughtfully. "We need you to continue being our Messiah, but it's not wise for you to walk alone. In future I'll have to insist several of our men stay with you." His offer of protection was little more than a cordon of jailers.

"Armed disciples?" I mused.

"They'll be armed, but I leave it entirely up to you if you want to teach them your ways," he spoke with little enthusiasm, satisfied that I'd be removed from speaking openly.

"How soon do you intend to move?" I asked.

"Soon," he cautiously answered.

"Soon?" I pointedly repeated.

"At Sukkot, the festival of the Tabernacles."

"When all Jewish men must attend the Temple," I completed.

"That'll be the best time to show our hand, so all Judaea will see," he spoke, pleased with the simplicity of the plan.

"But also, when the Roman Governor reinforces the Jerusalem Garrison - for exactly that reason?"

"There won't be any armed incident, so there'll be no reason for the Romans to interfere. Joseph has a plan to openly discredit the Sanhedrin."

"And that is?" I prompted.

"There are things even I'm not told - like you," he offered by way of consolation.

"And how do you intend putting me on Herod's throne?" I asked.

"Herod isn't our King," he spoke, offended.

"A Tetrarch by any other name - is still a King," I offered.

"Perhaps," he reluctantly conceded, unhappy with the thought. "By prophecy," he returned to my question..

"We have so many?" I queried.

"Zechariah," he simply stated.

"*Shout with gladness?*" I queried. Peter nodded.

"'*Shout with gladness, daughters of Jerusalem! See now, your King comes to you,*'" Judas interrupted. Peter looked to him so that he should continue. "'*He is victorious, he is triumphant, humble and riding on a donkey...*'." Judas was thrilled that this should be the plan.

"Where all the other pilgrims will walk, you will ride!" Peter spoke. "The way has been well prepared."

"'*He will proclaim peace for the nations*'," I continued the prophecy. "'*His empire shall stretch from sea to sea.....*'".

"Your arrival won't go unnoticed," Peter continued with suppressed enthusiasm. "The political statement won't be lost on our people - or the Sanhedrin."

"You'd confront them head on like that?" I asked, dubious of the wisdom.

"All the people will recognize the prophecy," he continued. "And the Sanhedrin will be forced to support Herod's claim to the throne - which has no strength with the people."

"The people will be moved to our cause, without direct confrontation with the Romans," Judas added, delighted with the plan.

"Our men will be well placed," Peter added, fingering the edge of his sword.

"What kind of a leader is it that says *follow me* and only a donkey listens?" I mused aloud.

"A leader who, in different times, might address open hearts," Judas replied, trying to sound encouraging. "Our hearts have been held by the Roman fist for too long."

"And do you believe such a day will be born - from the blood of others, Judas?" My question impaled Judas' reasoning and he fell silent. His dark eyes were torn between looking to me in apology and looking to Peter for support. Frustrated with himself, Judas looked out towards the darkening waves.

Having traveled for some distance, Peter suggested we pull ashore and stretch our legs for a while. High above a rocky escarpment two men and a dog watched our progress against the prevailing wind. Below them a herd of ruminating pigs ignored our approach entirely. Pulling the boat ashore, we began to walk upwards towards the herders. Suddenly, a huge and powerful naked-man emerged from a nearby cave. The cave appeared to be an abandoned tomb, though in more recent times seemed to have been used for sheltering animals. The naked-man ran toward our group, screaming and leaping over boulders. He then ran straight at me, abruptly stopping and throwing himself down on his knees.

"Rabbi, why do you come to disturb me, here among the dead?" he challenged.

From one arm hung a broken shackle and remnant of a chain. His ankles were bruised and sore, as though he had smashed and wrenched irons off them. The cuts on his chest and the bloodstained and tangled body hair, all amounted to a terrifying figure. Still on his knees, he stared up, almost daring me to respond.

"Why have you come here? What have you to do with me?" he screamed.

"What is your name?" I asked, stepping back a pace.

"My name is Legion - because we are so many," he manicly laughed.

Seeing the threat of evil, Peter made a move to protect me. I waved him back. A look from me again reminded Peter that his authority lay in the battle field, not here - in matters of Spirit.

"Legion, I command you, in the name of the Holy Spirit - leave this man!"

"In God's name," Legion spoke in a strangely quieter, yet higher-pitched, voice. "Say we won't be harmed. Don't torture us!" Peter and the others moved back, not wanting to have anything to do with this devil incarnate. Again and again the voice repeated itself. Almost as abruptly as it had begun, the voice stopped and then gained some composure, before speaking again. "Let us escape to the pigs - send us to the pigs? Yes, yes - that's what you must do - send us to the pigs!"

Legion's voice had that peculiar pitch of a man possessed. Higher up the hill, we saw the herd of pigs feeding and tended by their owners.

"In God's name, let us enter the pigs?" he shrilly pleaded.

I quietly spoke a Sanskrit phrase I had learned in Jagannath and the herd began to move. At first they appeared to mill around without direction and then, one large boar began to run down the hill. As if pursued by a swarm of bees, all the other pigs followed suit, gathering momentum as they raced towards the edge of the low cliff. We watched appalled as the entire herd plummeted to their bloody deaths on the rocks below. Everyone around me was visibly shaken. Looking towards the pig herders, I knew I had destroyed their livelihood.

John looked down at Legion and saw that he had changed. He remained kneeling, blankly looking up at me and smiling. Confused, but aware that the mad-man that had greeted us was no longer, John ran to the boat and found a blanket. Returning, John carefully put the blanket around Legion's huge shoulders. Legion appeared unaware of John's action and simply stared up at me.

Shortly after, the pig owners and representatives from the local village approached us. They were not so much concerned with the loss of the pigs as they were about the change in Legion.

"Leave our shore and go away!" they angrily shouted. "These are unHoly deeds and we're a God-fearing people. Leave us in peace."

They gently but firmly lead us back to the boat and helped us aboard. As I stepped into the boat, Legion became very distraught and ran after us.

"I want to come with you Rabbi. Please let me stay with you?" he helplessly pleaded.

"No, you can't come Legion," I spoke as gently as I could. "Return to your family and tell them about God's mercy. Your days of living among the dead have ended."

Legion smiled with love and the memory of his - 'til now - long-forgotten family. He continued waving long after the breeze had carried us far from shore.

Moving further South, I traveled only with Peter and eleven others. The main force would follow several different routes - so the Romans wouldn't become suspicious. Being close to Sukkot, the Feast of the Tabernacles , thousands of people were converging on Jerusalem and many traveled in organized groups. I enjoyed that part of the traveling. It gave me an opportunity to know my 'disciples' better.   I found a great thirst for spiritual matters, especially with Paul, Judas and Matthew. Peter always kept himself a little bit distant.   Despite his objections, he was well aware of being 'Joseph's man' and didn't want to become too familiar with me. While he honored my beliefs and teaching, he clearly considered me a rogue elephant among his carefully laid plans.   Judas spoke openly about his plans to return to the monasteries of Sinai *'after the Romans pull away from the shores of Judaea'.*

Paul seemed to have a special affinity with women.   I never saw a man with more impassioned views about the equality of women than him.   He sat comfortably with them and would listen for hours.   He wasn't patronizing, he simply cared.   He had attracted a number of women to our group, especially those that had suffered at the hands of the Romans.   It was too common a story in Judaea: the rape of Jewish women by Roman soldiers.   Initially the rapes were reported to the Temple Elders and the women received sympathetic hearings.   Over time, it became evident that the responsibility of legislative reaction lost all inertia once it arrived at the feet of the Men in Black.   Naturally they issued edicts of how women must dress, somehow implying that the women themselves had urged on the Gentile soldiers - soldiers who didn't know better!   To my knowledge, no Roman ever received punishment for the rape of a conquered people. Paul was a quiet man by nature and was cared for by an older woman, Anna, who I at first took to be his mother.   Anna had six children and had been abandoned by her husband many years earlier.   Apparently, as a child, Paul had seen her sorry circumstances and managed to supply her with enough food to support *all* her hungry mouths.   This was rare enough in any man, but for a child of twelve years of age, as he had been then, it was truly remarkable.

On more than one occasion Paul had drawn my attention to the fact that no women were ever directly taught the Torah. They were even segregated in the Temple.   Whatever they learned, was indirectly from hearing others debate.

"They're not considered intelligent enough and are systematically excluded" he complained.   Put so starkly, it *was* outrageous.   In our society, more than two women seen talking, would immediately be considered a conversation of trivia or domestic concern. In the Temple it was always taught that women were either mothers or seducers of 'honest' men. Women were not even allowed to talk to men outside of their immediate family. I hadn't consciously observed this subordination, before Paul insisted on it. Once pointed out, I recognized the intrinsic fear men held and the subtle ways they managed to exclude women. The fear stemmed from separation from their mother's breast. Many men felt the rejection and, when given an opportunity to influence society, expressed it unconsciously, through subordination of their mother's gender. Few men felt the wholeness that all men should feel. Paul's light reinforced in my own life, Man's need for love and forgiveness - both of himself and others.

On one occasion, our group was stoned by a group of young children, none of whom was more than eight years of age.

"Why do you want to harm us?" I asked.

"Because you travel openly with women who aren't your wives" one child called back, before running off. How sad that such bigotry could be taught to children so young. Even more sad was the fact that the child who spoke was a little girl.

Early one morning, a messenger arrived. Whatever news he carried was clearly of some importance, because Peter nervously paced back and forward as the messenger spoke. In the distance and further down the hill, a small delegation of fifteen or so people headed towards us. Peter broke away from his conversation and came over to speak with me.

"Do you know any Centurion's, Yeshua?" he spoke, handing me half of the flat bread he was eating. After the meeting he had just had, he was far too casual for this question not to have had significance.

"Not that I remember," I answered directly without question.

"Or their servant's?"

"Again, not that I know of." Peter fell into a silence while he thought.

"Have you visited Capernaeum?" he asked, looking down the hill to the approaching delegation.

"Many times," I answered. "I was there on my way back from Egypt. What's your real question Peter?" By now he was used to my being direct and so didn't attempt to be evasive.

"These people," he indicated to the approaching delegation. "They've been sent by the Centurion who commands the Capernaeum barracks." His look was directly towards me, almost accusing.

"You haven't spoken secretly with anyone about our plans, have you?" he asked in accusation. "If any Roman does learn about it, thousands will die!"

For some moments we held each other's gaze. Taking his hand and placing the point of his sword against my chest, I looked deep into his eyes.

"Do you know me so little , Peter? If you believe there's any truth in your accusation, I'll put my hands around yours as you push." Confused and embarrassed, Peter pulled away.

"How else can this Centurion know you're here? My men have been told to avoid towns and not to speak to *any* Romans!"

"They ask for me by name?" I queried.

Peter nodded and indicated towards the messenger. "He saw these people heading towards us and then overheard your name, and the Centurion's."

As the men arrived, I stepped forward to meet them.

"We're looking for Rabbi Yeshua?" the local Rabbi spoke.

"Your journey's ended," I spoke. "I'm Yeshua ben Joseph."

"My name is Marcellus and I bring a message from the Centurion of the Capernaeum barracks," a man beside the Rabbi formally began.

"And he sends a Rabbi?" I questioned in amazement, since the Romans were looked on as unclean Gentiles.

"I'm not *sent* by the Centurion," the Rabbi uncomfortably protested. "I choose, that is....."

His words were interrupted by the young man at his side who looked vaguely familiar.

"I'm a member of the Centurion's household. My master learned your name in the market place. It's said you're a great healer." As he spoke, I recalled seeing this man when I attended some sick children in Capernaeum.

"And what is it your master wants, Marcellus?   We're many days from Capernaeum and I'm traveling to Jerusalem?"

"The Centurion has been very generous in repairing the synagogue," the Rabbi awkwardly interrupted, attempting to recover his credibility with those around him.   Now I understood why he presented himself on behalf of a Roman.   A look from Marcellus indicated that it had taken considerable persuasion for the Rabbi to finally agree.

"A member of my master's household is near death.   He's brought up the Centurion's children as his own and is a good man."   Marcellus spoke with affection for the man.

"My master knows that you'd be defiling yourself at this time, by entering his household ...."   He hesitated before continuing.

"I explained our ways and that the Feast of the Tabernacles requires purification, prior to the festival," the Rabbi explained.

"Please," I requested.   "Ask me what you will."

"My master has heard that you're a good man and he asks simply that you place your thoughts on our friend."

"You come this distance, to ask so little?" Peter asked in disbelief and amazement.

"My words are few, but are chosen with humility Sir," Marcellus shyly responded.

"Why should we help *any* Roman?" Matthew asked.

"Here we have a man - true, a Roman; but one who has greater faith than those who have studied scriptures all their lives!" I spoke aloud.   "Marcellus, you have asked well.   With your first steps towards us, the illness which *was* to have ended in death, was postponed.   Return to Capernaeum, your master's servant is well and would speak with you."   In relief, Marcellus kneeled forward and kissed the hem of my sleeve.   As he did, I felt an inner jolt as I recognized the dark shadow of ego touch my heart.   I lifted him to his feet.

"This is God's work Marcellus, not mine.   A door is only useful if it can be opened or closed.   If it remains open, it is useless.   If it remains closed, it is also useless," I addressed Marcellus.   "The door requires people to move through it, or it serves no purpose.   This door needs no praise, it's simply there to serve."

His eyes filled with tears of joy and I held open my arms so that we could embrace.

"Yeshua ben Joseph, my master thanks you for his servant," he began, deeply moved that I would even touch his Roman hand. "And I thank you for this lesson in compassion. Your name will always be whispered in our hearts - you truly are a man of God." With that, he turned away and returned back down the hill.

The Rabbi expected to be asked to remain and have some refreshment at least. Peter offered none, so the Rabbi awkwardly offered his reluctant thanks and also left.

I walked away, needing to be alone for a few moments. I could see that Paul wanted to speak to me, but I didn't have the strength to face his questions. Several hours later, I returned. Our group had moved further down the hill towards the small town. Only Paul remained, now sitting with his back to me. He was unusual among the group, besides his constantly growing entourage of women. He was one of the few who wasn't training for combat. He was a devout Pharisee and from a wealthy home. At the age of fourteen, he had inherited a sea-going ship which traded with the Romans - much like Joseph's ships. The money, he used to further his spiritual studies. I even heard that he had studied with the grandson of the great Hillel himself! He always listened quietly when I spoke and rarely asked questions, yet I could see his eyes alive with curiosity.

"It's too hot for a goat on this hillside, let alone a Pharisee deep in thought," I spoke gently, so as not to startle him. He turned and I could see, tears had dried on his dust-blown face.

"I was thinking," he quickly explained - and realized his words were meaningless.

"You seem upset?"

He turned away in embarrassment. "Just thinking," he repeated.

"Such deep thoughts! If you'd been thinking of a rock, I doubt I'd have seen you sitting here at all," I joked. He smiled and thought better of his attitude.

"All my life I've been a devout Pharisee," he stated.

"No man's ever been condemned for that," I offered.

"Every minute of every day, has been guided by the Law of God," he continued with his heart almost breaking. "There's never been a time, when I haven't been able to react in a way directly specified by scripture."

"So why are you alone on this windswept hill - with your head in your hands?" I asked.

"How is it so easy for you, Yeshua?" he abruptly demanded.

"Easy?" I inquired, confused as to what he was asking.

"Yes, easy," he almost accused. "The other day you said we should 'love our enemies' - on whose authority?!"

"There is only one true authority," I answered.

"And earlier, you defiled yourself by embracing the Roman," he spoke with anger.

"It was my choice," I defended, surprised at his anger.

"You see!" he pointed out. "You make such a decision without any reference to the scriptures."

"I hear your words, but I don't understand your anger?"

"My life has been governed completely by obedience to the law and yet you....you...," he broke off, unable to complete the sentence and turned from me. I put a comforting hand on his shoulder and felt the immensity of his pain.

"Do my actions offend you Paul?" I asked.

"No, no," he spoke shaking his head. "Your actions show that my life has been an empty shell, filled with worthy words that weren't even my own. Yet, you appear from nowhere and it's as though God speaks through you." He sobbed deeply into his cupped hands.

"You think I appear from nowhere?"

"I've never heard your name mentioned in the Temple," he qualified. "Beside having the bloodline of David in your veins, what qualifies you to speak truth? Why has God chosen you?"

How could I possibly explain what I didn't fully understand myself? I could talk about former lives and initiations, but that would merely be words. Paul's heart yearned for a golden light which, though dimly flickering in his heart, could only be fanned by his own actions. Even if I was able to reveal the light for him, it's for each of us to realize for ourselves, that we are not separate from God.

We have merely forgotten.   Enlightenment is a boat that carries no passengers.

"I don't have any better qualifications than you Paul," I answered. "My blood has become a blessing and a curse."

"A curse?   You'll be put on the throne of David and you look on it as a curse?" he asked in disbelief.

"You think I choose this?" I indicated our friends below.

"But they work to put you on the throne?" he spoke, confused.

"God has placed me at the center of these plottings," I answered.   "If it were my choice, I'd remain in the mountains of India.   All paths lead to God, Paul.   Some are clear like yours, others aren't."   He appeared to gain some comfort from my words. More and more now, I noticed that when I spoke, my words - which may not have had evident significance to me - seemed to reverberate with others.

In the following days I noticed in small ways, how Paul was throwing off the religious strictures that had previously guided his every waking moment.

"You've split the shell of my chrysalis," he said when I asked him about the changes.   Even his walk became lighter, as if he had previously been carrying a literal weight.   Others became closer to him, drawn unconsciously towards the burgeoning light.

After the evening meals, he seemed to seek out my company.

"I've never heard a Rabbi speak the way you do Yeshua," he spoke one time.

"The content, or the delivery?" I asked, intrigued.

"Both," he answered. "You talk of Prodigal Sons returning to feasts, when any man of principal would reject such worthless offspring."

"Worthless?" I asked.

"And you talk of servants gambling their master's money - and being rewarded for it," he continued, ignoring my reference to anyone being 'worthless'.

"Oh, the parables," I spoke, now understanding.

"Yes, the parables. Your stories defy logic. Why? What's the purpose?" he asked with heartfelt confusion.   "Are they simply meant to irritate?   Take the story of your 'Good' Samaritan for instance. Everyone knows that Samaritans are less than the Gentiles. They've murdered hundreds of our people. They hate us and we hate them - yet you make them the hero of your story, above the servants of the Temple. What could be the purpose - other than to ridicule the authorities. These stories offend everyone." His final comment was said with care for my well-being, not from personal grievance.

How should I answer? Would explaining that I wanted people to see as innocent children again help? How should I explain that that lost innocence *could* be regained, and was essential in experiencing God's love directly. Would that help ease his confusion? I thought not.

"Sometimes I say things so that people might be forced to question their long-held opinions. I want to challenge their cultural bias. Their minds are fixed in time. Spirit is not that limited." He thought carefully before responding.

"Then why not in grander terms? You talk about mundane stories of tax-collectors and farmers. Why not talk of heroic figures in scripture that people look up to? Wouldn't that get your point across more effectively?"

"No, because heroes sit on pedestals, removed from most peoples lives. By talking about 'mundane' tasks, the mind is drawn into a trap and evokes moral outrage - before the mind can recognize it is being manipulated."

"Is that...ethical?" he tentatively asked.

"You have just answered the question," I replied. "You brought your understanding of ethics to my words. You made a judgment of mind - based on social conditioning. We are always judging! What right do we have to judge others?"

"If God doesn't make judgments on the way we live our daily lives, then what right do we have to judge others?" he cautiously queried.

"Exactly!" For someone of Paul's religious discipline to understand, I felt encouraged.

Often I found my self speaking of things I had no conscious knowledge of. Many times I found myself listening with interest, to my own words, words that I was hearing for the first time myself. Spirit moves in mysterious ways and I often find myself overcome with a bliss that seems to enter the tip of my skull like silver rain. Through Yoga practices I had learned to release all tension from my body and allow the bliss to settle and blossom in my heart. On two occasions, Paul had come across me wrapping my arms lovingly around myself. Had anyone else observed me, they would have taken my actions for extreme vanity. Paul recognized the love I felt for this so-limited physical body and the great privilege of incarnation it offered soul. As far as I knew he never mentioned it to another human being. For that alone I deeply respected him. Yet there was far more to this gentle Pharisee than was ever shown.

It was a welcoming sight to see the Temple walls again. Jerusalem had a way of resonating with the heart. Even my breathing took on a slower rhythm - I had come home. Although I had never lived inside it's walls, I always felt Jerusalem was my spiritual home on Earth. The very fabric of the stones beneath my feet, whispered of the scriptures and the wailing from the Arab quarter, beat out a timeless rhythm to the day. There was an energy about this ancient city that was unique. In some mysterious way, I knew it held the key to mankind's evolution. If the strife of different religions wasn't resolved in Jerusalem, then it wouldn't be resolved anywhere on the planet. Jerusalem was the key.

Since my time in the Great Pyramid, I felt that there was some huge cosmic secret in the Temple stones. I had the sense that this secret was hidden in plain view for all to see, but that only those pure in heart would ever see. What that secret was, I had no idea, but felt that I had some part to play in its revelation.

With Peter's help, I made inquiries about my cousin John. I had heard he had been arrested and wanted to know if I could help him in any way. Judas came across some of John's followers in the market place and arranged for me to meet them.

"They wouldn't speak with me because they're afraid of arrest," Judas said. "When I mentioned your name, they agreed to meet."

"Did they say where John was held?" I asked.

"No. Herod has so many dungeons, it could be anywhere."

"Where do we meet?" I asked.

"By Solomon's wall," he answered. "There's so much renovation work going on that passing strangers won't attract attention." Peter agreed that Solomon's wall was a good place to meet.

Hurrying to our meeting, we came to the sheep pool of Bethzatha. A crowd of sick and elderly lined the edge of the pool. Some people even shared the shallow water with the travel-weary animals.

"How can they share the same filthy water?" Peter asked in disgust.

"It's said that when the water bubbles red, the first man to enter the water will be cured of any illness," Judas explained.

"Have you seen it?" Peter asked.

"No, but I've met men who claim they were healed," he answered.

"Faith can move mountains - isn't that what our Rabbis say?" Peter spoke without conviction.

"You don't believe?" I asked.

"I believe in God and I believe in the power of Nature," Peter answered. "As for the curing of disease, in waters that have been contaminated by stinking sheep?" Although Peter was always pragmatic - as a soldier should be, his skepticism kept him from seeing spirit actively working all around him. However he did have considerable insight into human nature and it showed in the manner in which he adroitly handled his disparate forces. How sad that he should put up walls of resistance, against accepting the direct hand of God above reasoned coincidence.

To one side of the crowded pool, an elderly blind-man lay waiting on his make-shift bed. Even the thinnest sheep appeared better fed than him. As we passed by, I felt myself drawn back to speak with him.

"Excuse me good sir, how long have you been waiting here?" I asked.

"I've waited beside these blessed waters for nine years," he spoke, barely moving his cocked ears away from the dark and turbid water.

"After nine years, don't you wonder at the truth of this water?" Peter interrupted, scarcely hiding his skepticism.

The man smiled, aware of Peter's disbelief. "I have known it work for others," he simply stated.

"But who looks after you?" Judas asked.

"I'm blessed with a good family and they bring me food," the old man answered.

"So the waters haven't worked?" I asked.

"I don't know," he answered. "I've heard the water bubbling, but there isn't anyone to help me into the water in time. It isn't easy to move from this bed and others are younger?"

"Yet you still believe?" Judas asked.

"I have the faith," he answered. "That's why I stay so close to the water's edge - even with all these animals around me. My dream is that one day, Jehovah will allow me to be the first."

"Your faith will cure you old man," I quietly confirmed. Bending down, I picked up some dust from the ground and spat into my hand. Rubbing the two into a thin paste, I then applied my hands to the old man's face and eyes. He put up his hands to protest, but then allowed me to proceed. After waiting nine years, he was prepared to indulge this stranger for a few moments. He had nothing to lose. Reaching into the water, I then washed the paste from his face.

Leaning close to the man, I spoke so that only he should hear.

"Now pick up your bed and return to your family. These waters hold nothing for you."

Peter had already moved on, while Judas remained. As the man's sight gradually returned, we both moved away and followed Peter. Blinking against the bright light, the man's eyes followed our movement. After nine years of darkness, he was still afraid to leave the water's edge, even though it no longer held any purpose for him.

I later learned that this same man had been confronted by a group of Sanhedrin. He had been recognized as the blind man from Bethzatha Pool. Seeing him carrying his bed, they accused him of 'working' on the Sabbath. Because he was about to be punished for blasphemy, the man claimed that I had ordered him to carry the bed. What a strange creature is man and what a short memory! He claimed he had been content to sit for those nine years beside the Pool and that I had actually *ordered* him to reclaim his sight and carry the bed!

One of the accusing Sanhedrin had been a witness at the healing of the man in the synagogue. From the blind man's description, the Sanhedrin had realized I was the same man who had shamed their Rabbi in the synagogue.

When we arrived at the Temple walls, the sun had climbed high in the sky and beat mercilessly down on the lower courtyard. With construction work evident all around, the pilgrims made their way through the labyrinth of huge and untended cut blocks that were casually positioned around the base of the West Wall. How eager the people were to press their prayers between the stone crevices. Everywhere people looked to the ancient scriptures or to the vague future. How sad that so few looked to the present moment. Standing off to one side, two men watched us closely. By their rough clothes, it was evident that they weren't from Jerusalem. On seeing Judas, they indicated that we should continue walking and not make any deliberate move to speak with them. As we continued down into Kidron valley, the men fell into step beside us.

"We chose not to speak openly," the one later identified as Nathaniel spoke, "because we've been watched - and too many of our friends have disappeared."

"What can you tell me about my cousin?" I eagerly asked without turning to them.

"You are Yeshua ben Joseph?" he asked with excitement.

"I am," I answered. "What news of John?"

"He's being held secretly in the dungeon's at Machaerus," the other later identified as Jacob answered. "He often spoke about you, Rabbi Yeshua."

"What charge is he held on?" Peter asked.

"No charge," Nathaniel answered. "For him to be charged, Herod would have to admit he holds the Baptist."

"How long has he been held?" Judas asked.

"A little more than a year. I saw him captured," Nathaniel spoke with shame. "I stood by and let Herod's men take him."

"What happened?" Judas asked.

Nathaniel looked to Jacob, but wouldn't answer.

"They arrived after dark," Jacob spoke. "Eight men arrived, saying that they had traveled many days just to see our Holy Man." Jacob looked to Nathaniel to see if he would take up the story, but Nathaniel declined.

"They were dressed like any other pilgrims - except they had weapons hidden under their cloaks," Jacob continued. He paused a moment and looked down at the ground before continuing. "One of our members then took them to John - and he was seized."

"Why do you think he was taken?" Peter addressed Nathaniel.

"It's no secret," he answered. "He openly spoke against Herod's marriage to the Gentile Herodias."

"And that's enough to be thrown into a dungeon for more than a year?" I asked in utter disbelief.

"He's lucky to still be alive," Peter spoke knowingly. "Herod normally murders anyone who opposes him."

"It must be some time since you saw your cousin?" Jacob inquired.

"It wasn't so long ago, but we had been apart for many years before," I answered.

"While he taught around the Jordan, thousands came to listen - hundreds became his followers," Jacob continued. "He had become very influential."

"Even so," Judas interrupted.

"Herod sent many warning messages about the criticism - but John, instead of modifying his speech, went further," Nathaniel continued. "He claimed that Herod had murdered his own brother so that he could take his brother's sister for her Jewish blood - it would legitimize his claim to the throne."

"He also told people not to pay their taxes, since Herod isn't in the true line of David," Jacob added. Peter and Judas both looked to me, recognizing that I was also about to be placed in that same position.

"That alone would seal his death warrant," Peter agreed. "The fact is, it's true, but timing is everything." Peter shook his head at such unwise and rash behavior.

"I can understand him removing John - because the Romans might start to doubt his authority with the people," Judas quizzed. "But why has he kept John alive? It isn't like him."

"He's kept alive because Herod knows that if a single hair on the Baptist is harmed, the people will openly disclaim him and his whore," Jacob explained.

I was horrified to hear all this. "Is there anything we can do?"

"The Baptist will be kept 'till the end of his natural days," Nathaniel spoke with a heavy heart.

"There must be something?" I asked in desperation.

"He often spoke about you Rabbi," Nathaniel continued. "He said he'd come to prepare your way."

"How could he know about our plans?" Peter asked suspiciously as he looked to me.

"There are ways and ways," I answered. "John didn't know about your plans. I am a Rabbi," I simply stated and Peter appeared to understand.

"Rabbi, if you'll have us, then there are hundreds who'll follow," Jacob spoke with enthusiasm. As he spoke, I thought of India and the thousands of 'devotees' who would love to see me dead. Peter immediately became suspicious of Jacob's motives, but then realized the opportunity of adding more arms to his cause.

"Why would you want to follow me?" I asked. "It may be true my cousin's a wild man, but he's a man of peace. Look at me, I travel with armed men." Both Peter and Judas moved defensively as if to deny the swords beneath their cloaks.

"We've traveled all over Judaea, Rabbi and heard many strange things in connection with your name. For that alone, we'd be honored to serve - but you were proclaimed by the Baptizer and that's reason enough." Nathaniel spoke as if no more need be said. Judas was intrigued to hear more, but Peter indicated towards several Sanhedrin guards that were pointing in our direction.

"We've also heard it said that the son of David is being prepared for Herod's throne," Jacob added. Peter reacted as if he had received the full force of a spear in his chest. He slightly stepped back from our group.

"How do you know this?" he quietly demanded, keeping an eye on the soldiers above.

"Rumors - which you just confirmed," he answered with a smile.

"And if it's known to you, then to how many others!" Peter spoke with exasperation in his voice, in some way suggesting I was to blame.

"Then our journey isn't wasted," Nathaniel spoke with undue reverence.

"We're being watched," Peter spoke looking out into the valley. "It's time to leave."

"You followed the Baptist for love of God," I spoke. "With talk of armed men, you'll follow me for love of Israel. Don't think this way lies peace. In my wake, brother will kill brother."

"You speak very strangely for a Rabbi, but we still want to stay with you - if you'll have us," Jacob answered.

"You were called by my father and his word is my bond," I answered. Both quickly kneeled down and prepared to kiss my hand but Peter managed to stop them in time.

"There's a time and place," Peter explained, looking to the men watching above.

"It may not come to war," Judas interrupted as he watched four Sanhedrin join the soldiers looking towards us.

"The olive branch has been replaced by the sword - and Peter is my right hand," I spoke, waiting for Peter to contradict me, but he remained silent.

Above us, the man from the Pool who had had his sight restored, joined the group of Sanhedrin. This time they specifically pointed towards me and I could see the man confirm their questions.

"You there!" one shouted down to us.

"Don't attempt to run," Peter spoke, barely moving his lips and pretending he hadn't heard. It was obvious that with their spears and, holding the upper ground, we were fairly easy targets if they should so choose.

"You there, Rabbi!" they again shouted. From the clothes we all wore, it could only be me they were addressing.

I looked up and could see the old man was being restrained from either side.

"If we all move slowly off up the valley, they might let us leave," Judas spoke without looking up.

"No," I said. "You continue on and I'll go and see what they want."

"That could be suicide," Judas angrily whispered.

"If they take you," Peter threatened. "There'll be more than just *your* life at stake!"

Looking into Peter's eyes I knew I had no choice.

I walked as slowly as I could up the hill, without making it evident to my onlookers. If I was to be seized, at least my friends would be given enough time to make their escape up the valley.

"Is this the one?" the Sanhedrin I recognized from the previous temple spoke.

"I *see*," the old man spoke, attempting to struggle free from his captors. "Why should I accuse him?"

"Think carefully," the Sanhedrin spoke again, with cold threat in his words. "Were you committing blasphemy on the Sabbath - or were you ordered by this Rabbi?" As he spoke, the Sanhedrin's eyes watched mine, as a hungry hawk might watch for a small mammal. The old man looked away and spoke so low that I couldn't hear. The Sanhedrin seized the old man's jaw and forcefully turned him towards me.

"My hearing fails me," he spoke with false consideration. "You'll answer so that the Nazarene can hear!"

"This is the man who ordered me to break the Sabbath," he confirmed, with words that were too precise to have been his own. Out of the corner of my eye, I saw my friends climbing the opposite hillside, well clear of any spears.

"Are you the Nazarene known as Yeshua ben Joseph?" the Sanhedrin demanded.

"We've met before, and you know I am," I answered.

"I ask you again," he tersely spoke. "Are you the Nazarene known as Yeshua ben Joseph?"

"I am."

The guard moved forward to seize me, but the Sanhedrin put up his hand, suggesting his action to be unnecessary.

"What is the charge?" I asked. The Sanhedrin looked surprised. At that moment and much to my surprise, I saw Joseph arrive. It appeared no surprise to him that I had been detained. He joined the other Sanhedrin and was quickly informed as to what was occurring. He gave no indication of recognizing me. The first Sanhedrin turned back to speak.

"The charge? Blasphemy of course! An educated man such as yourself must know the Lord's day is sacred." He spoke with a smile at his lips, but none in his eyes. "As a member of the Temple I demand to know on whose authority you forced this old man to break the Sabbath?"

"I'm surprised at a member of the Sanhedrin not knowing his own scripture," I answered, aware that I was going beyond the bounds of safety. "There is only one authority - my Father's."

Joseph's face turned ashen as his eyes appealed for me to modify my speech. The Sanhedrin drew back in shocked amazement. "You would dare use those sacred words!?"

I realized that by claiming to be the Son of my Father, I had claimed direct descent from God. To me it was obvious that we were *all* direct Sons of God. To the Sanhedrin, I had claimed a lineage that even the High Priest wouldn't dare claim.

"So you don't deny it?" he asked, remembering his mission.

"How can man deny Creation?" I answered. "You search the scriptures as if, in those dry dusty words, you'll find salvation Sanhedrin. Can't you see? You're like the desert frog that looks up from the well and says the world is circular and only four feet across."

Without warning, he brought the back of his hand hard across my face. I felt the warmth of blood between my teeth. "You dare compare a Sanhedrin to a desert frog!"

"There are none so blind as those that will not see," I spoke, wiping the blood from my lips.

The Sanhedrin paced in front of his armed guards, shaking his head in disbelief. "Again you presume to lecture us, Nazarene?"

"No," I answered, aware that the guards were prepared to seize me at the slightest provocation. "No, I presume to show you the Word of God! This man, who was blind, bears witness to my calling. These armed men - and the mob, bear witness to yours!"

The Sanhedrin indicated for the guards to take me, but Joseph intervened. Speaking with words I could only just make out, Joseph pointed out that, by leaving me and putting the case formally before the Court of Sanhedrin, there would be no mistakes in judgment. This case was too important for this Temple member to act on alone, since it called into question the very fundamentals of the Temple. Uncertain at first, the man allowed himself to be persuaded by Joseph. He turned towards me and again smiled, this time with his eyes as well. His case was proven as far as he was concerned and I could be arrested at the Temple's leisure.

"Then we'll detain you no longer Nazarene," he spoke magnanimously. "Your words have given us great comfort and we must leave - to prepare your way." The guards and the Sanhedrin abruptly turned away and returned towards the Temple. I found myself alone, facing Joseph.

"You have failed us Cousin!" he spoke with great disappointment. "Our men aren't ready to move yet and you've condemned yourself." In answer to an inquiring call from the departing force, he spoke as he walked away. "Those that have seen the blood of their families dry on the ground, won't forgive you this day Yeshua!"

Joseph hurried after the others and the smile on his face belied the words he had just spoken.

I stood for some moments and knew I had stepped on the ladder of destiny - from which there was no retreat.

"It's good to discus theology with people, but for you to defy the Sanhedrin at this time, is madness!" Peter slapped his hand against his forehead, as he might wish to strike me. "Joseph will tell us when to move! You're warning them to prepare for trouble, Yeshua. Don't you understand?"

I looked around at the small gathering and saw few sympathetic faces. Paul appeared to understand and I could sense him inwardly cringing as Peter spoke.   John also sided with me, though he never spoke. Judas was torn.   On the one hand he wanted me to confront the Sanhedrin, but on the other, he wanted me to hold my tongue.   Time is an enigma that few men understand and Judas was becoming impatient with me.   He agreed with my confronting the Sanhedrin, but not with my timing.

"I know it took courage to speak as you did, Yeshua," he reluctantly acknowledged.   "But you put us all at risk - everything we've planned!   That courage will be needed when you're on the throne, not now."

"We can't take any more chances," Peter finally spoke.   "In future Yeshua, you'll have an armed guard with you at all times."

"For whose safety?" I asked.

"For all the sons of Israel!" he answered defiantly.   Both Paul and Judas volunteered.   Ten others were also delegated.   As the twelve were appointed I thought of the Little Mother of Allahabad and her words. *"Key to everything is the number twelve.   Everything exists in relationship to everything else.   This planet is a Great living Being that requires mankind to evolve, so that it also can progress spiritually.   With your coming, people will understand the power of three.   Your purpose is to take that understanding to the power of twelve, the true key to the spiritual world.   Through twelve the spiritual world is made manifest - mark this well!"*   Although thousands of miles away, her words were as clear as if she had been standing beside Peter.   There would be a perfect symmetry with my armed guards.   As I placed my attention on this thought, I had an instant and total understanding of how each person fitted into this crystallized action.   Each person was essential to the outcome of the overall plan Spirit had formulated; yet I still didn't have clear insight as to what that action might be.   It was as though I walked through a fog of Spirit - it was evident all around me, but had no precise form.

Joseph sent word that we were to remain camped near the city walls, but not to take any action that might draw attention to ourselves.   The men were relieved that they didn't have to stay cooped up inside the city walls, particularly with the lack of moving air at night.   In the evening, a cool breeze funneled up the Kidron valley to the gardens where we were camped. It was a good time. I was able to talk in greater depth about the teachings I had come across in my travels and the wonderful things I had seen. My 'guards' soon became my closest friends. Even Peter listened intently, still retaining a certain distance so that he wouldn't be compromised with his allegiance to my Uncle. We remained until the Feast of the Tabernacles. Although still accompanied by guards, I was allowed to attended the Temple. With the thousands of pilgrims constantly passing through its courtyards every day, our small group drew little attention.

How the Temple priests reveled in their authority! Many of them were good men and guided the people well. Others appeared more absorbed by politics and the influence they could exert. Caiaphas the High Priest appeared a reasonable and wise man, but he surrounded himself with the politicals of the Temple. Perhaps that was the reality of the times - the real rulers were the Romans and the Sanhedrin were forced to play the political arena in order to survive. How hard it still was not to judge others!

I watched as Caiaphas entered the Holy of Holies. He entered the curtained room, with the rope of gold around his waist. If he were not a pure vessel, Yahweh would strike him dead. His purpose was to hear the word of God and use it to guide the peoples of Israel for the coming year. In my lifetime, no High Priest had ever needed his assistants to pull on the golden rope. No body was ever pulled from the Holy of Holies.

It was while the final ceremony was in progress and all power had been bestowed on him by the Sanhedrin Assembly, that I could hold my tongue no longer. These men looked to the empty ceremonies and not to the Living God for whom the ceremonies were dedicated!

"If any man is thirsty, let him come to me and drink!" I shouted above the chanting. Inwardly I heard the words and outwardly I found myself shouting, as if in a dream. The words were expressed without thought intervening. All heads turned towards me. Had I tried to stop the power of Spirit acting through me, I knew the physical body would be severely damaged at a very subtle level. I recognized that I now identified more with the words of Spirit than I did with this outer physical shell. My delegated 'guard' moved nervously around me, hoping I might be ignored.

"Anyone who believes in me, shall have rivers of life run from them," Spirit continued and I marveled at the words. Several of my friends put restraining hands on my arms, but I wouldn't be silenced. The Sanhedrin were mortified that, not only had I interrupted their final ceremony, but I had laid claim to divinity.

The Sanhedrin member who had tried to arrest me above the Kidron valley, cut through the massed crowd with a handful of heavily-armed guards.

"Enough of this desecration!" he shouted. "Seize that man and take him to be stoned!"

"I am the light of the world and anyone who follows me, will never again walk in darkness," I continued shouting as Peter and Thomas stepped nervously in front of me. Naively, they thought that by shielding my face, my words might not be heard.

"It's the Nazarene the Baptist said was to come!" a man in the crowd shouted. At first one or two spoke out, then others called out in resounding support. The Sanhedrin stopped his men, fearing a possible uprising against the Temple.

"If a man keeps my word, he will never know death," I heard myself shout out.

Another member of the Sanhedrin stepped forward and Peter blocked his passage to me. "We heard you were a wise man Nazarene? Yet clearly we're wrong, you're possessed! Even our father Abraham knew death. Do you claim to be greater?"

"My Father, who you claim as your God, is the one who honors me," I answered in defiance of his arrogance. "Your father Abraham rejoiced when he saw my day."

Many of the Sanhedrin moved forward to surround me, incensed at my words. "Then clearly you are possessed!" he continued. "You're not even forty years of age and yet you claim to have seen Abraham. Give yourself up to the guards and leave this place for honest men to worship."

"Good Rabbi, in truth I tell you, before Abraham was born - I am!" This was the sacred phrase which God alone was permitted to use and now, they were intent on vengeance. A surge of men pushed forward with the sole intent of seizing me and carrying out the decree of stoning.

Peter quickly organized a cordon of his armed men to surround me and, if necessary, fight our way out of the Temple grounds. Suddenly Joseph stepped forward and held up his arms.

"Wait!" he shouted. By his robes, he was immediately recognized as being among the ruling members of the Sanhedrin and the guards held back. "I recognize this man with the Nazarene," he pointed towards Peter. Peter's eyes widened in alarm. "Aren't you a member of King Herod's household?" Peter and his friends no longer concealed their weapons. The Sanhedrin held back, not daring to lay hands on a member of the King's own household. Peter recognized his cue and spoke confidently.

"I am," he replied.

"And what are you and these armed men doing in the Temple with this blasphemer?"

"We are members of King Herod's personal guard and have come to the Temple to arrest this Nazarene. He is charged with treason against the state of Judaea."

The crowd had little love for the King and many words of descent were heard. The Sanhedrin were confused by this strange turn of events and looked curiously at the men with Peter.

"But you dress like Galileans?" one asked distrustfully.

"Our master sent us to the Galilee, to learn who this man's friends are. That's why we dress like this," Peter answered.

"Now that you've arrested him," Joseph prompted "what is the sentence?"

"He'll be executed tomorrow by the King's own executioner," Peter answered - now confident enough to turn his back towards the armed guards and look directly at me.

"Then it seems to me," the first Sanhedrin spoke. "We should delay your progress no longer. Attend to your duties so that we can attend to ours." Joseph melted back into the crowd, while the Sanhedrin cleared a path for the 'arrested prisoner' to be taken. Mark and John seized me forcefully by the shoulders and dragged me quickly from the ceremonies.

It was no longer safe to remain in the Gethsemane garden. Joseph sent word that we should immediately leave Jerusalem, before the Sanhedrin learned that no prisoner had ever been delivered to Herod. He would also have to be very careful, since he had initiated the 'supposed' arrest.

"You must be more careful, Yeshua," Peter spoke as we walked towards Qumran. "You still haven't understood! The people look to a military solution to our throne, not a religious one."

"Perhaps the time is right for us to take up the responsibility of *being* the Chosen People," Paul interrupted on my behalf. Although he hadn't been in the Temple to see the fury of the Sanhedrin, Paul supported my actions. He and Judas had become close friends and often argued the merits of a spiritual solution as represented by me as opposed to a political coup as represented by Joseph and Peter.

"I agree that ultimately we need the nation to be guided by a spiritual leader," Judas argued. "But it's been more than a thousand years since Solomon sat on our throne and here we are - still a suppressed people."

"Because we haven't had a true spiritual teacher at the head," Paul answered, equally passionate. "They were all elected by the existing system. No matter which way you prune an olive tree, it will only produce olives. We've had a thousand years to learn that this tree that we've tended won't produce sweet fruit."

"Then you agree with me!" Judas rejoined. "We should replace the entire system and start again."

"We agree on the solution, but we differ on the method of achieving it," Paul answered. "If a child begins his education under the threat of punishment for not studying, everything he learns from that time on will be conditioned by that pain." I smiled as I listened. Paul had grown so much since we had spoken on the hillside.

"But it's a small price to pay if his attention is focused on the end result, which will benefit him for a lifetime," Judas argued, unable to see Paul's point of view. "If we seize the throne by force, then we can choose our own spiritual leader."

"And how does that differ from Herod's method?" Paul asked. Judas laughed, realizing he had cornered himself in argument.

"Yeshua," he appealed. "Don't you understand what I'm trying to say?"

"I understand exactly," I answered. "If a child is troubled by disease, then there *is* a case for painful medicine. You look at the child who is crippled and say 'the leg must come off'!"

Judas held up his hands in defense. "Now, I think that's overstating my case!"

"In Spirit, Judas, there is no degree of 'rightness' or 'wrongness'," I answered. "A thing is either right, or not."

"Can Israel afford to wait another thousand years?" he asked, as if the answer were evident.

"Time was invented by man and is a further separation from God," I answered.

"You feel no sense of urgency?" he asked in frustration.

I recognized the urgency he spoke of. There was a sense of unease in the atmosphere - an air of expectancy. Judas appeared to sense this more than most, but his interpretation was misguided.

"No," I answered. His look of disappointment towards me suggested I wasn't the man he had thought me to be.

From that time, Judas never looked at me in the same way. We exchanged views, but now he distrusted my actions. While we continued walking, Judas walked ahead, preferring to be alone with his thoughts.

Peter waited until there was no one close at my side before speaking again.

"Yeshua, I must emphasize - we need a *military* solution, not a spiritual one," he quietly spoke. "That's why all these men are prepared to put their lives in your hands. You don't have the right to throw it away!"

"Are these Joseph's words?" I asked.

"They are, but every man who stands with us, will confirm those same words," he spoke dismissing Paul's earlier argument. "Our land has more zealots than there are olives on a tree - we don't need another, at this time. There will come a time when you'll be able to speak freely, but not now."

"So, has Joseph's plan changed because of my actions?"

"The plan remains the same, the timing has changed," he answered. "We'll now have to wait until the Feast of the Passover. The Sanhedrin are too prepared right now. In time they will lower their guard."

"I'm still to be King?" I asked.

"Joseph believes you're the most suited," he reluctantly answered.

"I'm to be your Trojan horse?"

"You'll be carried *by* our horse," he answered without apology.

"And you won't speak out in the Temple again?"

"Can you be so certain?" I asked without threat.

"If your face is recognized, you'll immediately be put to death. The Sanhedrin don't easily forget," he spoke with some confidence. "And a wise man doesn't kill the beast that carries him!?"

"Joseph chose you well Peter," I answered his implied warning. We continued walking. "Sometimes I'm directed by an inner voice...I have no choice in my actions. Where I can, I'll comply with your wishes, but please be patient."

"And I also forget," he spoke with sadness. "We've trained for little else these past years, but you.... I realize it can't be easy - finding yourself at the head of an army." Paul came alongside as we spoke.

"Am I interrupting?" he asked, looking to both Peter and myself.

"No," Peter answered. Paul appeared pleased that he had chosen a good moment.

"There's something I'd like to ask, Yeshua," he spoke hesitantly.

"Before you do," I interrupted. "There's something I'd like to ask you?"

"Anything," he offered as pleased as a puppy with two tails.

"Peter and I were just discussing my role as leader of an army. Do you think I'm suited to the part?" I asked looking to Peter.

"I wouldn't automatically think of you, in connection with battle," he cautiously replied, also looking to Peter.

"Peter thinks I am that man," I teased. "Who do you think I am?" Paul seemed embarrassed by my question and wouldn't answer. "Come," I prompted "you're among friends."

"Some have said you are our beloved Elijah, born again," he paused before continuing. Peter looked surprised. "Others say you're the prophet Jeremiah."

"Such august company," Peter stated, tolerant of Paul's beliefs.

"And who do you say I am?" I pointedly asked.

"I haven't studied the scriptures like Judas and can't say," he reticently offered.

"But you have some thoughts," I again prompted. "If I'm not the leader of these men you see here, then who am I?" Peter raised an eyebrow, intrigued to know Paul's opinion. Seeing that we both wanted to hear, Paul was forced to answer.

"My heart burns with a fever when I stop to consider, Yeshua ben Joseph."

I stopped in my tracks, forcing both men to also stop. Walking up to Paul, I cupped his cheek lightly with my hand. "This truth hasn't been revealed to you by men, good Pharisee. I have come to bring a fire to earth, and how I wish that it was already lit!"

We continued walking and allowed Peter to walk ahead. He had sensed that I had more to say, but that my words were meant for Paul alone. When he was out of hearing range, I put an arm around Paul's shoulders.

"There is a Baptism ahead, Paul and I'm deeply distressed until it is completed. What it is, I can't say - not because of any distrust, but because fear blocks it from my consciousness."

"You fear?" he asked, surprised.

"I feel a great void," I quietly answered. "To step out into the Unknown and face the reality of God, is to be consumed by a terrible Love. To face God in human consciousness, the personality you speak with now, must be obliterated and merged into All Being. The voice you speak with - fears that loss of identity." We continued walking. Paul hung his head in deep thought as he attempted to comprehend my words.

"Don't think I come to bring peace to this torn land," I raised my voice so that Peter ahead, could hear. "I don't come to bring peace to Israel, I come to bring a sword!"

"That's what the men need to hear," Peter called back over his shoulder.

"You've answered my question Paul, but what about yours?" I asked, remembering his original purpose.

"Just beyond Qumran, there's a small community," he began. "I have some old friends there and I'd be very honored, if you would come and visit?"

"I'm not sure that Peter will allow me to wander," I answered in view of recent events.

"It's beyond Qumran - and further from Jerusalem," he offered hopefully.

Paul had been right and Peter didn't insist on my having an armed escort. The main body of men camped on the shores of the Dead Sea, while Paul and I turned North.

"You'll have much in common with Lazarus," Paul unnecessarily encouraged. "He's traveled among the Temples of the Sinai and spent several years in Egypt."

When we arrived, we were warmly greeted by Mary and Martha. Mary was a large and powerful woman. Her sister Martha was considerably smaller, but was the real strength in the relationship. Martha allowed her bigger sister to believe she was the driving force.

They were overjoyed to see Paul. "Our favorite Cousin come at such sad times," Martha spoke. "And this must be the Rabbi from India?" Both Paul and myself were surprised that she would know who I was.

"How did you know Yeshua?" he asked. "We only decided to come here yesterday?"

"Our brother spoke about you," Mary confidently spoke.

"How could he know?" I asked.

"There are a lot of answers we don't have, good Rabbi," Martha spoke looking sadly to Mary. "Why has our brother been so suddenly struck by illness?   Why has he taken to the family crypt and refused all food?"

"And why has he called your name?" Mary quietly added. The question was directed at me as if I might know. Paul looked to see if I could throw any light on the mystery - I couldn't.

"What illness?" Paul asked.

"We sent doctors to him, but he sent them away," Martha answered. "Two weeks ago he went to the market and bought new robes - the old ones were less than a year old! When he returned he went to each member of the family and bid us farewell, as if he was leaving again."

"He took no food or drink and went to lie down in the crypt," Mary added.

"What madness is this?" Paul demanded. "Why isn't he in the comfort of his own bed? Perhaps it's a sickness of the mind?" he ventured.

"No," Martha firmly stated.   "He made legal provision for everyone - in the event of his death. He's forty two and in the best of health - or was. He simply said he had the need to lie with his ancestors. We're his sisters and he's head of the household, how could we disobey?"

"I'm sorry to bring you here at such a sad time," Paul spoke turning to me. "But I still don't understand how he knew you'd be coming today."

"He repeated," Martha continued. "'The Rabbi from India will come, the Rabbi from India will come.....'"

"Has anything unusual occurred in the past few weeks?" Paul asked, trying to gain any insight into the illness of his old friend.

"Not while he's been in Judaea," Martha replied.

"He's been abroad?" I inquired.

"Yes," Martha replied. "He just came back from travels in the West."

"Where in the West?" I asked.

"The Sinai and beyond," she replied.

"To which counties, Martha," Paul urged, understanding that I wanted precise information.

"I think he mentioned Luxor," Martha spoke hesitantly.

"Egypt! Did he mention any other names," I asked without trying to sound excited.

"He mentioned some name, but it was unfamiliar to me," Martha shook her head in regret.

"He mentioned staying at a small temple in the desert," Mary offered.

"Did he call it by name?" I asked.

"That's right," Martha interrupted. "He did mention some temple, but I don't remember the name." She also shook her head.

"Does the name Zoan sound familiar?" I cautiously asked.

"That's it! That's the name he used - wasn't it Mary?" Martha spoke excitedly.

"It *was* Zoan. I remember now, because his eyes looked strange when he mentioned it," Mary spoke with new found confidence. "I just thought he was tired from his travels - but, it means something to you, Rabbi?"

"I stayed there a short time in my youth," I answered blandly, so as not to raise their hopes. I recalled happy times eating fresh dates before dawn and playing with my cousin John. How life had changed since those days of innocence. Then we played without a care; now I lead an armed force, about to turn Israel into a sea of turmoil, while my cousin rots in some forgotten dungeon.

The women expected more from me, as did Paul.

"Has he shown any sign of sickness before?" I inquired.

"Lazarus the Ox, we used to call him," Mary quietly spoke.

"There wasn't a stronger man and he only ever rested on festive days," Martha proudly proclaimed.

"Then I believe this illness won't end in death," I offered. Both women were completely confused. They neither knew whether to thank me, rush to Lazarus or offer travel-weary visitors some hospitality.

"Perhaps some wine?" I suggested to break their impasse. The water in that region, while edible, was a murky brown color and tasted too much of the earth. Mary rushed off to provide food and wine, while Martha took us to a shady table at the side of the courtyard.

"Should I call Lazarus?" Martha nervously asked.

"Let him rest a little longer," I answered. "He knows his Indian has come."

We ate in silence. The sisters barely touched their bread, anxious for their brother. I knew it would be too soon to approach the crypt. Merely by placing my attention on the body that lay in the tomb, I became imbued with the truth of the event. Lazarus had fasted for many days so that his body would be refined enough to undergo an initiation. The frequency of his spiritual vibration was being increased so that a greater light could pass through it. Had I directly approached the tomb, considerable damage could have been done to Lazarus' physical body, at the most subtle level. As we sat in silence at the table I became aware, that our parallel bodies of Light and Sound, were being brought into alignment. His consciousness would soon filter through his outwardly unchanged body. Inwardly, the Lazarus the sisters had previously known, would be no more. To their eyes, there wouldn't be any physical changes, but they would sense a profound change had taken place. He would seem more distant, yet more caring. At this watershed in history, as darkness grew in the world, greater beings of Light were emerging.

Mary could barely keep still, repeatedly offering forward the wine jug, while my glass remained already full. Martha gently took the jug from her and smiled apologetically towards Paul and myself. Finally Mary couldn't take the silence any longer.

"Rabbi," she abruptly started. "You say this sickness won't end in death, but...." Before she could finish the sentence, a frail and death-like figure appeared at the entrance of the family tomb.

"Lazarus!" Martha quietly whispered, holding her small fists to her mouth. Shocked, both women remained rooted where they sat. Lazarus leaned heavily against the opening. I rushed from the table with Paul close behind.

"Yeshua," Lazarus whispered in the weakest of voices, before falling unconsciously into my arms. Had it not been for his words I would have doubted that *any* life remained in this frailest of bodies.

After carrying the body to his bed and making sure that some liquid passed his lips, Paul and I left, despite the sister's protest.

"How did he know you would come?" Paul asked as we traveled South. He wanted to know so much. How could I explain the unexplainable? I'd have to use words where symbols were necessary. I'd have to speak of frequencies of light - of which he had no experience and no reference. He wanted knowledge of things that could only be comprehended through direct Wisdom!

"In God there is no separation," I explained in terms that might come closest to what he needed to know. "Being and God are one. There was never a time when Lazarus didn't know. Light removes the scales on our inner sight." My words were inadequate for what he required at the conscious level, yet they reverberated deep within his soul and he asked no more.

Around me as we walked, I heard the words: *"A child may pick up a stick and in his mind's eye it becomes a sword, with which he can duel in mortal combat. By telling the child the reality of this same act, now carried out in maturity, would we dissuade him from play? For you to talk of Initiation and the raising of consciousness, would men not still call it death?"* I looked to Paul to see if he also heard the voice, but he appeared oblivious. There was a curious familiarity about the voice and I thought of Maitreya.

After returning to Peter's camp, we remained several days, simply resting.

"I've been hearing strange stories, Yeshua," Peter casually spoke as he poked a stick into the fire one night.

"We live in strange times," I responded with a smile.

"Indeed," he firmly replied. James and Matthew studied my face with uncharacteristic interest.

"Strange stories?" Judas inquired, always eager to hear the unusual.

"Raising men from the dead," Peter casually spoke into the flames.

"That certainly is unusual," I responded without further comment.

"What would you say about it?" Peter inquired with undue innocence.

"There's a world of difference between possibility and reality," I acknowledged.

"Not a thing that happens every day," Peter continued as he watched Paul's reactions. "Many people restore sight to the blind, but to return life to the dead - that, is unusual."

"In the job of a bookkeeper, a man of action might well believe himself to be dead," Paul joked.

"And what do you say, Yeshua?" Peter directed towards me.

"The perception of death is not always as simple as we are sometimes told," I answered. "In India I knew men who were able to stop their heart at will - and suffer no harm. Our doctors would have declared them dead. Would our doctors have been liars or simply mistaken in their perception of truth?"

"But these are rare exceptions," Peter contended.

"And even rarer, is the *perceived* returning of life to the dead," I answered. "What makes the extraordinary extra-ordinary, is that normal rules don't apply."

"Perceived or not," Peter brusquely continued, aware that I wasn't going to say anything further on the subject. "The Sanhedrin have also heard the rumor."

"That's not good for us," Judas concluded. "Before, they could dismiss you as just another wandering Rabbi. Now, these rumors will bring you to their attention again, but as a real threat to their spiritual standing." Although Judas spoke in warning, he couldn't hide his enthusiasm for the confrontation.

"Joseph believes they have a plan to capture you Yeshua," Peter solemnly added. "He hasn't heard it directly, but we have to question your viability as our future King."

Judas jumped angrily to his feet. "What cowardice is this?!" he demanded. "Yeshua has given up a life of spiritual study so that Israel can have the blood of David on our throne! We've forced him into this position and now - at the first sign of hardship - we cut him loose for the dogs!"

"Judas!" Peter stood up to directly face him. "Because you're the leader of the Iscarii, doesn't give you the right! This isn't *'the first sign of hardship'* as you well know. Hundreds - perhaps thousands, have been endangered by Yeshua's actions!" Judas reluctantly acknowledged that what Peter said, had some truth. Still he believed Peter was overreacting.

"Then I offer my life - if any other is put at risk by Yeshua's future actions," Judas dramatically offered.

"You would do that?" Paul asked, astonished.

"I've done it for others far less worthy," Judas confirmed. The faces around the fire looked at each other in impressed disbelief.

"I thank you Judas, but you don't know what you offer," I spoke, standing up. "It's an offer too great for me to accept and too great for you to understand. Whatever's decided by Joseph, I'll agree to. If I'm to leave, my wife and I will never again see the shores of the Galilee." With that, I walked out into the clear night and left behind the heat of debate. The night sky always held a deep comfort for me. The perspective of the all encompassing heavens absorbed my ego like healing balm. Those same stars I saw above me, also looked down on the Hemis monastery in India and the Great Pyramid of Giza. How insignificant my destiny felt against the clear and vast canopy of stars that stretched beyond the infinite and brilliant Milky Way.

The following morning, I returned to the camp feeling rested and regenerated. Peter was already up and preparing for the day. He watched in silence as I approached.

"You sleep so little," he spoke between splashing water on his face.

"With so much at stake, I'd have slept less in my bed," I answered.

"I should have taken your lead," he spoke with a welcoming smile.

"You were troubled?" I inquired. He dried his face before answering.

"I've known many battles, Yeshua," he began with hesitation. "I never lost sleep at the thought of my own possible death - it comes to us all, and the choice is mine."

"But -?"

"But you, Yeshua," he spoke opening his hands towards heaven! "All my experience tells me that we should part ways!"

"You've decided?" I hesitantly asked.

"No! No I haven't decided!" he firmly answered. "In a sense, it's been decided for me."

"I'm to leave?"

"No. You're to stay," he answered. "I *was* going to send word to Joseph that you should leave, but a messenger came earlier and the decision has been taken out of my hands."

"A messenger from Joseph?" I asked.

"Yes - and there isn't enough time for me to send word and then get a reply back."

"Before what?" I asked.

"Before we act." Although he would rather I left the movement, there was a sense of relief in not having to commit to his decision.

"When do we move?" I asked.

"Today. We return to Jerusalem today." From the rocks and surrounding scrubland, men rose to face the day somehow sensing that this day might be their last.

"There's something you should know, Yeshua," Peter continued ominously.

"From your tone, it's not something that'll will bring me comfort?" Peter shook his head in sorrowful agreement.

"Your Cousin - the Baptist......"

"John? What's happened?" I asked, expecting the worst.

"He has breathed his last."

"He died?" I asked in disbelief - that someone so vibrant could no longer draw breath.

"Murdered," Peter simply spoke. "Herod had him executed. His head was cut off!"

"But why - why now?" I asked.

"This is only known to the Sanhedrin. The people don't know yet. If they did, God only knows what might happen."

"So this is why Joseph says we're to act now?" Peter had no answer to my accusation. "How did it happen?"

"There was a feast at the Palace and too much wine," Peter spoke as carefully as he could. "Herod is known to have more than a father's interest in his own daughter - and she asked for the Baptist's head on a silver plate."

"Why would she ask such a terrible thing?" I asked in amazement.

"We don't know for certain, but we can be fairly sure her mother Herodias' hand is somewhere behind this."

"Herod's wife?"

"The Baptist's made no secret of his feelings about her. 'Herodias the Whore', is a common expression - thanks to your Cousin," Peter spoke apologetically.

"John never knew that sometimes, discretion is the better part of valor. What was in his heart was always less than a breath away from his tongue. I've never known such a heavy loss."

"The people loved him," Peter spoke, putting a comforting hand on my shoulder.

"And that's why we act now?" Peter nodded in agreement.

"Joseph will announce it when we're ready. The people will be behind us when they see how their leaders have kept this information from them. By his death, your Cousin has changed the destiny of Israel."

Perhaps unfairly, I was disgusted that my Uncle should try and profit from the death of one of God's purest children. By his mere presence and example, John had taught me so many things. It was him that explained the need of pitiful and destitute children. He had always been conscious of the great souls who chose to incarnate in those emaciated and deformed bodies. He suggested it long before I had the understanding.

"By their piteous deformities, they teach us compassion - the teaching of the Heart," he had said. In some curious way I felt he had deliberately dressed so offensively - by Judaic standards - so that men should also question their reactions to *his* appearance. His life was a lesson. At that moment I understood how much of an inspiration he was to me. I also realized that to honor him, I could do no less.

The closer we came to Jerusalem, the greater the number of Pilgrims there were on the road. Our number of about two hundred, appeared less obvious since the men deliberately formed staggered groups. Judas walked beside me.

"When you're on the throne Yeshua, *everyone* will see the Kingdom of Heaven," he spoke earnestly. His words were so shocking I stopped in my tracks.

"What?" he asked, surprised at my reaction.

"Your words, Judas!"

"Its the truth," he answered defensively. "Now we'll have a spiritual leader to lead the Chosen. God will show his hand and the righteous shall govern the land."

"The Kingdom of Heaven is *not* coming Judas," I spoke, barely daring to voice my thoughts. Judas became mistrustful.

"Not coming?" he questioned. "Are you saying that you won't fulfill your promise to act as King? Many men have placed their lives in your hand this day, Nazarene." His sudden anger showed in his use of the word Nazarene and I caught a glimpse of a man I hardly knew.

"I will act as King," I answered to calm him. "The Kingdom of Heaven is *already* here, Judas."

"Already here - that's ridiculous! Do you think good men who have lived their lives in desert monasteries would be unaware, if that were true."

"I can't answer for them," I simply answered. "God's truth does not relate to time. If you think it is to come, then you don't recognize what is. Look around. Do you think that merely by placing me at the head of the nation, everyone will suddenly have the scales lifted from their eyes?"

"I don't like your words, Yeshua," he fired back at me, as if I had accused him of the most dire crime. "It is written. I've trusted you - and I don't give my trust lightly."

"And I have trusted you, Judas. Can't you see - as long as man expects the hand of God to intercede for him, man will never accept the responsibility for being the direct Son of God. There is no separation between me and my father, Judas."

"This is a trick of words Yeshua," he spoke putting up a hand as if to deny my truth.

"It's no trick," I answered as I recognized his anger rise.

"All this, is for nothing?" he asked in horror.

"All this is for man - and Joseph," I answered.

201

"How can you dare say that?" he demanded. "You, with the blood of David in your veins. Don't you believe we're the Chosen, as promised to our Father Abraham?"

"Every man is 'chosen', Judas," I answered.

"No, you're wrong," he spoke, shaking his head. "Some are chosen to right injustice."

"And are you one of these?" I quietly asked.

"It's plain you're not the man I took *you* for, Rabbi Yeshua. You may not have the courage to face up to your destiny, but I intend to face mine." His words stung my heart with their intensity and I stood back from him.

"Judas, you've seen God's hand act in healing - why do you ask when his Kingdom will come? Open your eyes! God's Kingdom is all around us now - not tomorrow." My words were intended to ease Judas' mistrust, instead, they served to strengthen his suspicion of me.

"Is anything wrong?" Paul called over. Judas stepped away from me.

"Ask our friend, the Nazarene!" Judas answered in anger and walked away in disgust. We continued walking. Judas walked ahead, occasionally looking back to see where I was. From his manner, it was as if he expected to find a knife plunged into his back at any moment. Paul walked silently beside me, but never commented on the separation between myself and Judas.

By midday, the sounds of the merchants reached our ears. We had come within shouting distance of the city walls. The whole southern end of the Temple wall swarmed with hammering masons and men carrying heavy materials for supports. Huge blocks of stone were being hauled up long ramps, before being carefully positioned. Some of the blocks dwarfed even those I had seen in the great Pyramid. Close by the southern entrance, Peter pointed towards a tethered donkey.

"There's our statement," he proudly announced. "One that'll be recognized by any true born Jew, yet will go unnoticed by the Romans." All along the parapets and entrances, armed Roman soldiers stood in readiness for any trouble. "Some of our men have gone ahead and prepared your way."

Paul walked with me to the donkey, while the others quietly entered the city walls to take up their positions.

"He's well fed and watered - and needs to be," Paul spoke, commenting on the fact that none of us had eaten or drunk since leaving our camp many hours earlier. "Today he carries the burden of history!"

"Yet which one of us is the beast of burden?" I softly spoke into the animal's twitching ears. Paul looked surprised.

"But today you might become King?"

"And you might become a soldier, Paul," I answered. In his wildest dreams, Paul had never taken up arms and knew that I was suggesting it would *also* never happen.

"But our men will be with you in the temple, when Joseph makes his announcement?" Paul seemed shaken that I believed events might not go according to Joseph's plan. He was banking on the fact that many of the people had heard about my 'raising the dead' as he put it. It was too accidental that so many should have heard and I recognized the hand of Joseph at work. That, and the statement I'd be making by entering the city walls on the back of a donkey, instead of walking, as the other thousands of pilgrims did. Joseph was prepared to announce my claim to the Judaean throne and had positioned many of our men among the Temple audience. If the Sanhedrin stood against us, then our armed men would take the Temple by force.

At my insistence, Paul remained outside the city walls.

"*Behold your King comes to you*," his words of encouragement followed me, "*humble and riding on a donkey.*"

Even before I passed under the stone archway, it was obvious that the people had been prepared. Hundreds lined the route to the Temple, throwing palm fronds in front of the donkey's feet and shouting out "*Hosanna! Blessed is the King who comes in the name of God!*" Among the crowd I saw several Sanhedrin angrily arguing with the people and demanding that they stop their actions. One young Pharisee ran up and demanded that I order the people to stop desecrating the sacred festival.

I handed him one of the many garlands that had fallen on my tunic. "Pharisee, I tell you, if the people remain silent, the very stones will cry out!" The Pharisee remained behind, stunned by my blasphemous words. Suddenly Peter appeared at my side, helping to clear the route ahead.

"Isn't this the most glorious day, Yeshua?" he laughed. I had never seen Peter in such good humor.

"The people are very generous but, in forty years, their cheers will turn to tears," I spoke as I too heard these inner words. "Jerusalem will be destroyed by fire and thousands will hang from Roman crosses. Look well how the people are fed and happy - tomorrow will be very different."

"Tomorrow will look after itself!" he spoke, angry that I didn't share his new-found optimism.

"Tomorrow is born from today," I answered with a heavy heart. "The people look to the table in front of them, not to the coming harvest." Peter again disappeared into the crowd, confidant of Joseph's plan. "There is a wind that comes from the North, that brings no man any good - and I feel its first touch on my cheek."

On the high wall above, several soldiers pointed down towards me. To them, we Jews were nothing more than rats trying to squeeze into a space that was too large for ten times as few Jews. They had no comprehension of how sacred this land was to us. One of the Romans spat, trying to hit the donkey or myself. The spitting hadn't been consciously offensive, it was merely an habitual action that many Romans used to point out their subjected peoples. From his raised eyebrows I could see he considered me to be one of the few sane Jews at this time - I was the only one sensible enough to ride on the back of an animal in this oppressive heat. How little he understood.

At the foot of the broad Temple steps, a small group of Peter's best men waited. Secretly armed, they were intended to be my unobtrusive bodyguard. As I dismounted, one took the beast while another lead me gently forward into the Temple. Mark stood forward to explain the planned events.

"After the High Priest has spoken, Joseph will stand forward and pronounce you the true heir to the Judaean throne," he spoke quickly. "If they resist, the people will be told about the Baptist. We'll stay close by so the Sanhedrin can't seize you."

"If there is any resistance, we're ready," Judas spoke, revealing the sword and knife concealed beneath his shirt. Even when he smiled, no light reflected from his eyes.

As we moved forward towards the Inner Temple, I saw several Sanhedrin recognize me. Realizing that I was surrounded by 'friends', they decided to rush off for reinforcements - before attempting to capture me. I indicated to Mark what was happening. He sent three men to intercept these Sanhedrin before they could reach the main body of the Temple. We were in the area of the outer courtyard, where the people sold the sacrificial lambs and birds - at great profit. The Sanhedrin kept one tenth of the sales, besides the profits made from money-changers who sold the Temple coin with which tribute *had* to be made. Among the vast crowd, I recognized Caiaphas the High Priest talking to one of the money-changers and felt a sudden rage run through my body. Leaving my friends, I rushed over to the nearest money-changer and upturned his table. Silver coins flew everywhere and eager hands from the crowd closely followed. In the ensuing chaos, I saw Mark's men seize the Sanhedrin and forcibly restrain them. People took little notice of the struggling Sanhedrin, since all attention had turned to the uproar at the money-changers' tables.

"What madness is this?!" Caiaphas' shouted out as he hurried forward, stopping the money-changer from attacking me.

"Priest, you dare ask me - a loyal Jew!" I shouted back at him.

"This is madness!" Caiaphas confirmed. "That any Jew should talk to the Temple's Leader in such a tone of voice? But your face *is* familiar, Nazarene?" It would only be moments before Caiaphas remembered who I was, so I decided to keep him off his guard.

"Priest, this house was ordained for prayer, not a meeting place for thieves!" I spoke, looking to the money-changers, who were now appearing in force.

"A meeting place for thieves!" Caiaphas spoke in disbelief.

"Can good and evil co-exist in God's house?" I demanded.

"How dare you!" he shouted, almost lost for words. "Do you presume to tell the High Priest who is good and who is evil?"

"For anyone who has eyes, the answer is self-evident," I answered and threw over another table. Curiously, Caiaphas was saving my life. Had he not been there, I would have been torn limb from limb by the angry money-changers. As it was, none dare move without direction from him. All around, hundreds of the poor, feverishly scrambled for the coins on the floor.

"On whose authority do you dare attack these poor pilgrims?" Caiaphas demanded, as he regained his thoughts. "The authority of this place lies with the Sanhedrin and I, Caiaphas the High Priest, don't recognize you."

I looked around at the troubled faces. Some looked hopefully towards me, others looked with hate.

"There's not a single loyal Jew here who wouldn't lay down his life to save this Temple from disgrace," I spoke, addressing everyone. "I simply act as a loyal Jew. You, Caiaphas, have sold our birthright for a few coins." I picked up several against my feet and flung them towards him. His face flushed with fury and he looked around for his own guards. In the melee, his guards were too dispersed to act coherently. Several of Peter's men managed to come and stand beside me, their weapons concealed, yet apparent. Caiaphas looked to the men at my side and recognized his own life might be at risk. The money-changers withdrew behind their tables.

"Come," Caiaphas spoke with less confidence. "This is no place for violence?"

"Violence of the mind carries deeper consequence than violence of the flesh," I answered. "It is less honest. Expressed, it is finished; kept in the mind's eye, it grows darker."

"If it wasn't the time of the festival, I'd gladly hear more of your 'philosophies' Nazarene, but now my duties call," Caiaphas spoke, turning into the crowd for safety.

"- And darkness follows!" I called after him.

"We shall meet again - Yeshua ben Joseph," he called back, now remembering who I was. As he tried to regroup his own men, so that they could arrest me, Caiaphas watched as Peter and Mark forcefully bundled me through the seething crowd and out of the Temple grounds.

The following hours were chaotic.   I was taken to a large building overlooking the Kidron valley.   The house was owned by a relative of one of our wealthy women and a close friend of Paul's. Peter had ordered that I remain hidden inside.

"It's enough that you betrayed us at our moment of triumph, but if the Sanhedrin capture you for everyone to see..." Peter spoke, unable to hide his anger.   "Then our whole cause is lost!   What use is a King if he's seen as a puppet before we even start!"

I didn't responded, because he wasn't prepared to listen.

"Because you created that diversion, Joseph wasn't able to address the Temple," he continued.   "We lost our best moment, because of you!"   Judas glowered in agreement.

Throughout the day, key members of Peter's men found their way to the house.   I remained inside the building and watched as the women prepared the evening meal - they seemed less judgmental than the men.   As they worked, we heard many stories of our men being seized.   Those that had seized the Sanhedrin members, had all been taken.   The main question was, were they going to be stoned, or would they be handed over to the Romans for crucifixion?   Without doubt, they would never see another full moon.

In the upper room, the twelve that sat at my table remained silent.   At the other tables, men spoke quietly, occasionally throwing looks towards us.   Women passed out the wine and tried not to speak about the day's events.

"Have you nothing to say to me, Peter?" I finally asked.   The entire room fell silent as he took an olive stone and placed it carefully at the side of his plate.

"Today is a day our people won't soon forget, Yeshua," he coldly spoke, looking up at the faces turned to our table.

"Nor should they," I answered.

"Mark is dead and eight of our men captured," he accused in a quiet but firm voice.

"And you blame me?"

"Who else?"   He spoke with the coldest of smiles.   A low murmur rose from the tables around me, many agreeing with Peter. A few called for me to respond.   Peter sat back, so that I should address the room. I stood up and looked into the expectant and accusing faces.

"Are there any here that don't think as Peter does?" I asked. Several people shuffled noisily at their tables - but none spoke up. "How easily we judge each other! Does our father in heaven judge us, or does he provide even for the Romans?" As I spoke, Judas got up from the table and left the room. "Our father doesn't judge us - we do that on his behalf! When we pass through the tunnel of light, to be with our maker, we'll all carry our own Book of Records."

"Everyone saw your actions!" Peter interrupted in frustration.

"But how many understood?" I asked.

"Since your judgment seems to be that of most of the people here, perhaps you'd say it to my face?" I offered.

"You made certain that Joseph couldn't speak!" As he spoke, his finger forcefully emphasized each word on the table.

"I also provided the distraction so that Mark could seize those men, once I was recognized! If they had reached the main forces, the whole Temple would have been sealed off in moments - we would all have been captured!" Peter had no answer, since he knew I was right. Many grumbled with my answer, not wanting to understand. "Our timing - Joseph's timing - was wrong!"

"You created too much attention before we even arrived in Jerusalem," Thomas suddenly spoke out. Thomas was very close to Mark and I understood his pain.

"We all loved Mark," I answered, addressing his unspoken statement. He was confused by my answer and turned away.

"We've thrown away the initiative," Peter spoke with some conciliation in his voice.

"Then we should act immediately," I offered. Peter's look to me suggested that my words might have an ulterior motive. At that moment Judas returned to the room. His eyes were caste down, sensing that he was interrupting an important announcement.

"What would you suggest?"

"The Sanhedrin will be searching for us everywhere, even now," I said. Peter narrowed his eyes sensing that I might have a plan. "It'll only be a matter of time before we're all identified. While their men are thinly scattered, we should appear openly in the

Temple and state our claim." Peter poured more wine as he thought over my suggestion. His eyes watched me closely as he drank. Putting the goblet down, he spoke down towards the table. "And will you play your part - for Israel?"

"I'll fulfill my destiny," I offered. Peter considered my words - and finally smiled.

He stood up and spoke so that all could clearly hear. "Let us raise our cups to Israel's new King!" Everyone stood and offered their cups forward. Everyone, except Judas. With everyone getting up, and some quickly sitting back down, no one noticed Judas.

"What's wrong Judas?" I asked. "Won't you join in our celebration?"

"The wine is too new," he explained as he held his head between his hands. "My head and stomach are not good."

"Come Judas," Peter goaded. "You'll always have a head and stomach, but how many times will you see the dawn of a new age?" Judas looked through pain-racked eyes, but wouldn't drink. I soaked some of my bread in the olive sauce and passed it to him.

"Eat this and drink less wine," I offered. He knocked the bread from my hand.

"Why should I trust you, Yeshua?" he pleaded, suddenly looking deep into my eyes as if to find some definitive answer.

"Why don't you?" I asked.

He looked around at the festivities before speaking. The pain in his head was evidently intense as he rubbed his temples. "You're a spiritual man, Yeshua. I don't know what to think.... In one breath you tell us to love our enemies - and now you provoke an attack in the Temple." His face pleaded with a desperate need to understand.

"I thought, in you I had found a true man of God.... I've killed many men, but you...," he stammered with passion for his unspoken beliefs. "You didn't just betray Israel when you attacked the money-changers - you betrayed me! I looked to you Yeshua - I believed yours was the way I never found in Sinai! You're just like any other man!"

Several at our table looked away from their conversations to see what Judas was upset about. I put my arm around his shoulder, but he shrugged it off.

"Won't you embrace me?" I quietly asked, so that only he should hear.

"Embrace you!" he spoke pulling away in horror. "You're a viper in our midst! Your actions cause more men to die than I ever killed - and you call yourself a teacher!" Although he tried to keep his voice down, he spoke through clenched teeth and few at the table didn't notice.

"Embrace me, Judas," I spoke firmly. "Tomorrow will live in the histories of all our peoples!"

"I'll have nothing to do with you! I thought you were different from the Sanhedrin.... You've betrayed me Yeshua!"

"Calm down Judas," Peter called from the other end of the table. Judas stood up abruptly, knocking several cups over.

"Embrace me, Judas!" I again repeated.

He staggered drunkenly from the table towards the door. "I'll have nothing to do with you or your plans, Yeshua." He held up his left hand, shielding his vision so that he shouldn't have to look at me before leaving.

"*Nothing to do with you or your plans,*" Thomas mimicked. He had also had too much to drink.

"Judas?" I appealed.

"Let him go," Peter called out.

I was keenly aware of him closely watching my reactions. I turned to Peter and gestured with my hands, so that he should call Judas back.

"It's nothing," he spoke waving down my concerns for Judas.

"Nothing?" I queried. "It's everything."

As the night drew in, too much wine was drunk by everyone.

"Joseph was right," Peter spoke, leaning heavily against my side. "The Sanhedrin won't expect opposition inside the Temple." I drank from the cup and Peter insisted on helping. Immediately I emptied the contents, he refilled it.

"Peter," I asked. "If I wasn't Joseph's choice, would you have supported my claim?"

"To the throne?" he drunkenly inquired.

"Yes," I answered, putting my hand over my cup as he tried to pour more wine. "- If there wasn't a force of armed men to back me up?"

"Of course," he answered without thinking, inadvertently knocking a dish of cheese to the ground. "Judaea should have a Jewish King."

"And if tomorrow, Joseph's scheme doesn't go according to plan?"

"I'm a man of my word Yeshua," he sat up straight, offended that I would even question his nobility.

"I've never doubted your honor Peter," I tried to placate. "What I ask is: if at the final moment, others desert my claim - will I see you standing at my side?"

"I have lead all these men here for one purpose," he spoke firmly. "You offend me by even asking?"

"Offend you? Peter, tomorrow before the cock has crowed three times, you'll remember these words."

"Sometimes, I wonder about you Yeshua," he spoke shaking his head in confusion. "In one breath you make an excellent suggestion of striking at the heart of the enemy and in the next......"

"You will remember my words," I spoke as a chill touched my heart.

My attention was abruptly drawn to the steady rhythm of approaching feet outside the building. Those that hadn't drunk too much also looked up, inquiringly. A few sharp words were heard from downstairs. Then, it seemed as if the door exploded off its hinges, as more than fifty Sanhedrin soldiers rushed into the room with raised swords. The soldiers quickly lined the walls and subdued any who might have the presence of mind to try and escape. Peter raised his sword and found several others, placed at his throat. No one spoke. One face I recognized from the Temple and presumed to be the Governing officer. He raised a hand towards the door and Judas entered. Without a word Judas walked around the tables and came directly to me.

"I'll take that embrace now, Yeshua," he spoke into my ear as he placed a kiss on either cheek. How dark Judas' eyes were. He seemed to look beyond me as if in a trance. I no longer recognized him for the brave-hearted warrior I had first met. With that simple act, he turned away and left the room. Several soldiers rushed forward and tied my arms securely behind my back.

"Traitor!" Peter called out and received the blunt end of a sword across the back of his head. As he fell forward, the officer-in-charge waved the point of his blade to everyone assembled.

"There'll be no further trouble tonight," he offered in return for an unimpeded exit. Being dragged forward, I knocked several tables over in the process. I was roughly thrown forward down the stairs, my head heavily striking the stone wall.

Immediately I was pulled to my feet and dragged outside the building. To my amazement, six hundred fully armed Roman soldiers stood in formation! The Romans were there merely to sanction the Sanhedrin's actions and make sure that no rioting broke out. How threatened the Romans must have felt - to allow an *entire* cohort of men to leave the safety of the city walls.

"So many soldiers for one man?" I asked.

The Legionnaire stepped forward and, using the full weight of his body, brought the back of his leather-clad hand across my face. The force of the strike knocked me off my feet and onto the ground, where I fell at Judas' feet. His face was wet with tears and he shook his head with disappointment.

"You betrayed me, Yeshua. You betrayed me," he spoke quietly through his tears.

"What is the charge?" I asked looking towards the Legionnaire.

"Charge?" he repeated, amazed that I would dare address him. "Pilate nears the end of his term - we don't need charges! If he's forced to stay and clean up any trouble, then you won't be the only Jew to regret this night."

I could hear the sound of footsteps running from the building behind. The Legionnaire prepared himself to take action, but then saw that the sound held no threat.

"Run back to the dark holes you came from," he shouted after the escaping feet. "And tell the other rats that Pilate won't be lenient with *any* trouble-makers."

"Why am I being taken?" I asked, clearing the blood from my eye.

"You'll have to ask the High Priest," he vaguely answered, still watching the darkness beyond. "We're here to make certain there's no riots."

"There's no rioting here," I objected. "You saw - we were just celebrating the Passover."

"Because I'm in a good mood, I won't allow them to kill you - yet," he spoke, leaning close and sharing a confidence that all could hear.

"The Romans are here to ensure the Law of the Temple is carried out," the leader of the Sanhedrin force spoke, coming forward.

"And what Law is that?" I asked. "And why have you come in darkness - at this sacred time of the festival? Is it so that people won't be able to see your dark deeds? Was my light so bright that you couldn't see me in the Temple this morning?"

"The prisoner will hold his tongue!" the Sanhedrin shouted into my face. His breath was foul from fasting. Seeing that the Romans expected some explanation of their actions, the Sanhedrin was forced to respond. "At this time there could have been bloodshed and, as leaders of the Temple, we wanted to spare our people. These soldiers are only our witnesses."

"My understanding was that witnesses only needed eyes and ears," I goaded. "So much witnessing," I spoke looking around at the Romans, "and so heavily armed!"

Not having any credible answer, the Sanhedrin also brought the back of his hand across my face. The strike moved me slightly sideways and I savored the blood coming from my lip.

"The might of Rome is greater," I spoke, comparing the two strikes. I addressed the Legionnaire, ignoring the Sanhedrin. The Legionnaire suppressed a smile and called out for the guard to march on. Two large Sanhedrin grabbed me forcefully by either elbow and prepared to march. With my arms tied behind and being pulled forward on either side, I was more dragged than walked down the rough path. The Sanhedrin seemed to take pleasure whenever I fell.

213

"The might of Rome is greater, is it Nazarene?" one asked with mock concern.

"That might be," the other spoke. "But your life hangs from Caiaphas' little finger!"

"And I think we can guarantee, all the might of Rome won't resist that little finger," the first added with a smile.

We traveled at a forced march for about one mile before coming to the gates of Caiaphas' Palace. The heavy and ornate iron gates clanged noisily in the night, as they were dragged across the cobbled entrance. The Roman guard withdrew, while the Sanhedrin Marshals continued on into the Palace. Practiced insults were spoken under the breath while the Sanhedrin watched the Romans march crisply off into the darkness.

After traveling down endless corridors, we came to a large assembly hall. On the raised steps, that ran either side of the Hall, sat approximately sixty members of the Sanhedrin - though the hall could hold at least ten times that number. The two guards threw me forward so that I fell on my face. Pulling my legs around, I managed to get to my feet. It was apparent that prisoners brought before this assembly would be expected to cringe in fear for their lives. I felt the fear, but stood tall and looked directly into the eyes of my judges.

"Thank you for coming," Caiaphas amiably spoke, stepping down from his raised podium to meet me.

"The high Priest's invitation, is by way of threat?" I questioned.

"A mere formality," he dismissed. I could see that the assembly didn't like the fact that *anyone* should address their High Priest in such a familiar manner. Their faces showed that my fate had already been decided and they expected subservience.

"Your magician's trick was very interesting this morning" he spoke, more for the benefit of his assembled audience than for myself.

"Magician's trick?" I asked.

"Vanishing as you did," he answered, again addressing the assembly rather than me. Suddenly, I realized what he was saying. For the High Priest to allow any 'blasphemer' to insult the Temple and then to escape right before the High Priest's own eyes - would not be acceptable to the ruling body of the Temple. In order for Caiaphas to save his dignity and credibility, he had made up a story of my being a Magician! Whether the accusing faces believed this preposterous story or not, it was expedient and didn't threaten their standing.

"Did you go to all this trouble, just so that you could see a second performance - from this humble street-performer?" I answered, showing the ridiculousness of his accusation. A flush of anger crossed Caiaphas' face and in that moment I knew, this was not a man to make angry.

"Silence Nazarene," he spoke changing his entire demeanor. Before, he had been falsely amenable, now he was coldly efficient. "As Appointed Elder to the people of Jerusalem, I order you to identify yourself and your supporters." I remained silent. Caiaphas walked slowly around me, wondering if he should speak again, since he realized I wasn't going to respond to his authority.

"Identify yourself," he almost whispered into my ear from behind. I remained silent and looked up at my seated, and silent, accusers. Caiaphas walked over to the front row of steps and spoke upward towards the assembly. "As a Rabbi, you know my office has the power to order your death by stoning?" On finishing his words, he casually wheeled round on his heels to see my reaction. Fear gripped my heart, but I knew that I was innocent of any charge and remained silent. Caiaphas was a politician besides being leader of the Temple and I knew that whatever I said, would be twisted to prove my guilt.

"Won't you speak in your defense, Yeshua ben Joseph?" he spoke, again changing his demeanor to one of deep concern.

"We know each other Caiaphas," I simply stated.

Caiaphas looked confused and turned to the Sanhedrin as if for explanation of my words.

"Know each other?" he queried. "I know no Jew who would *ever* attempt to destroy the Temple and its teachings!"

"I haven't spoken secretly of my calling and I haven't threatened the Temple. I've spoken openly in many synagogues. Why question me in this darkest hour? Question the hundreds who have heard me - they know my teaching." Again Caiaphas opened his arms, appealing helplessly to his audience.

"You see how he speaks to the leader of the Temple?" he offered. "And this, in the face of death. This man is dangerous for our people. He doesn't have the sanity to grasp life and preaches sedition!"

"Sedition?" I questioned. "Where's the sedition in demanding that thieves and robbers shouldn't be allowed to practice their trade in the Temple grounds. This isn't sedition - this is God's Law." Again Caiaphas threw out his arms to the audience, suggesting that even if he wanted to, his best defense of this prisoner wasn't sufficient enough to save me from the Stoning Ground.

"We've heard it said you're a man of integrity Rabbi? That you teach God's truth?" Caiaphas spoke, as if he was prepared to learn, yet behind his words I sensed a deadly threat. "We can see that you're not easily influenced by men - and care little for their position. Perhaps you'd be kind enough to enlighten us on one small point? Tell the assembly: is it right that we, the Chosen People, should pay taxes to a Roman Emperor?"

"Hypocrisy now!?" I answered. "Why do you try to trap me with these childish games?"

"Games?" Caiaphas held his hand against his chest as if mortally offended.

"Yes, games! You want to denounce me as a common criminal so that you can take me in front of Pilate, claiming I tell the people not to pay the taxes." As I spoke, Caiaphas' demeanor again changed. He watched me as a snake might watch a rat, waiting for the moment to strike. He turned and walked away, shaking his head in regret.

"For one who preaches compassion and brotherly love, I see little evidence of it in your manner, Yeshua," he spoke and then turned towards me. "An innocent question, is seen as a snake in your bed."

"Innocent!?" I spoke in disbelief. "You send hundreds of men, in the dead of night - during our most sacred festival - to arrest me......"

Caiaphas held up his hands to interrupt and protest. "You misunderstand me, Nazarene. They were there to protect you. There have been rumors of armed men outside the city walls.... You were only called here to....to clarify a simple point that has troubled our sleeping hours. This is no game."

"A 'simple point' that so many educated men should lose sleep?" I spoke looking around at the Sanhedrin members.

"Yes," he avoided. "Should we pay the Roman taxes?"

"Bring me a purse," I offered. Caiaphas gladly produced his own. "Show me a coin that you'd use to pay this tax." Caiaphas took a silver coin from the pouch and, with unnecessary flourish, displayed it for everyone to see. "Whose image is carved there?"

"You know it's the Emperor," he answered with indulgence. "Tiberius Caesar." Some members also took coins from their purses as if there might be any doubt.

"Then why do you ask me who it belongs to? Give to Caesar those things that are Caesar's and to God those things that are God's." As my words registered with the audience, many became indignant and made out that they had actually been looking for something else in their purses. "*This* is evidence of the Sanhedrin's collective wisdom: to send an army of men under cover of darkness to find this!?"

From the corridor I had entered by, some disturbance had broken out. Joseph entered, barely allowed access by the guards. Caiaphas raised his hand and beckoned Joseph forward.

"Our friend from Arimathea," he benevolently announced.

"I beg the council's forgiveness," Joseph spoke, catching his breath. "I only just received news about the meeting."

"It was convened at short notice," one of the administrative scribes called out by way of answer. "The messengers reported you weren't home."

"Not home - even though this is the Feast of the Passover?" Caiaphas spoke with a suggestion of recrimination.

"I was called to report to the Governor," Joseph answered defensively. "Some damaged fruits in his shipments," he explained. Joseph suddenly caught sight of me and almost froze in his tracks.

"It's good that you maintain such close relationships with our military rulers," Caiaphas spoke with some disdain. "Politics decrees that we can't always choose our bedfellows. As a member of the Sanhedrin, I'm sure you know on which side of the bed you sleep, Joseph?" Although it was spoken as a statement, no one listening had any doubt that this had also been a thinly veiled warning.

"I know where to look for my shoes," Joseph answered firmly, holding Caiaphas' look.

"Good," Caiaphas broke off. "I had no doubts - despite rumors to the contrary."

"That you had doubts, or that I had misplaced my shoes?" Joseph cautiously questioned.

"I forget," Caiaphas casually ignored. "It's of little consequence." To Joseph it was of great consequence, but he was too shrewd a man to push his point, particularly at this time.

"Why has this man been brought before the court?" Joseph asked as if confused by the whole event.

"Do we *really* need to explain, Joseph?" Caiaphas asked as if Joseph already knew.

"God has given us sacred breath and I rarely like to waste it by asking questions to which I already know the answer." Joseph spoke with a smile, yet each word was honed and found its mark with Caiaphas. Although deeply offended, Caiaphas thought for a moment as he paced in front of me. Then he stopped and looked directly into my face as he spoke, his words directed to Joseph.

"Correct me if I'm wrong Brother Joseph," he continued as he looked closely at the blood running down my cheek. "Wasn't this the Nazarene who the guards were going to arrest at the Kidron valley - before *you* suggested they think better of it?" He sharply wheeled to see Joseph's response. Joseph couldn't see what significance the question had, with regard to his question. "And wasn't it this same man that created the disturbance at the Feast of the Tabernacles?"

"I can't be sure," Joseph answered with far less confidence.

"Oh, I think you can," Caiaphas urged. "And if memory serves me well, I believe it was a member of the Sanhedrin also, that pointed out the member of King Herod's household that had been with this man - and again he was allowed to escape!?"

"You misrepresent my actions, Temple leader," Joseph loudly objected! "I'll demand a meeting of the Synod to hear these false allegations!"

Caiaphas casually turned to the Court Scribe and called out. "Did we schedule that for the Wednesday or the Thursday?"

"Thursday," the scribe called back.

"You see Joseph, unlike you, I *do* ask questions to which I already know the answer."

"But this man is held like a criminal," Joseph pointed to me as he openly appealed to the members. "It's against our Holy Laws to summon the Council during the hours of darkness - and during our Holy Festival? Must we defile ourselves to further the Leader's political ambitions?!"

"Political ambitions?" Caiaphas asked in amazement. "What higher position *could* there be than Leader of the Temple?"

"It's a wise man who knows he has enough - and power is *very* beguiling." Joseph's words sounded hollow in defeat. Few of the members were persuaded by his argument and those that were, knew better than to stand against Caiaphas.

"This isn't an official Council meeting," Caiaphas spoke, trying to return the discussion back to the matter in hand. "We merely heard that this wandering Rabbi might be leaving the area soon and wished to have the benefit of his wisdom, before he left."

"Yet he stands before you like a prisoner?" Joseph stated the obviousness of the situation.

"Do you presume to lecture us on the Law, Joseph?" Caiaphas demanded impatiently.

"The Leader misunderstands me," Joseph answered, attempting to sound submissive. "I simply wanted to be informed of the laws of which I'm apparently ignorant."

"I've always found that the best way to learn, is to remain silent - and listen. We can debate the finer points of this issue at a later date - perhaps, after your hearing!" Caiaphas was no longer prepared to be tolerant of Joseph and turned his back on him so that he should be seated.

"Yeshua the Nazarene," Caiaphas continued. "We ask you before the living God, are you another Messiah come to divide the people of Israel?" He turned away, not really expecting a reply.

"I am!" I answered. Caiaphas turned in shocked disbelief.

"You know that by using that Holy phrase, you stand condemned by your own tongue?"

I looked slowly around at the shocked audience. "You all stand fully condemned by *your* own words. I bear witness to the Truth - I AM!" The silence rang through the stone room and Caiaphas stood with his jaw half open, unable to believe his own ears. Finally he staggered backward as he pulled the robe from his back.

"Then the reports are true," he spoke in disbelief. "This Council is called to pass judgment!" With that, he stood on his formal robes and pulled at them until they were torn into several fragments. Holding the fragments above his head, he tossed them aside, to show his abhorrence of my blasphemous words. "The Council will vote!"

"We should hear what defense the Nazarene offers!" Joseph called out.

"Very well" Caiaphas offered. "We'll test him according to Isaiah." Caiaphas indicated to one of the ushers and a blindfold was produced.

"Since Joseph seems to look favorably on you, perhaps you would like him to tie the blindfold?" Caiaphas offered. I looked over to Joseph and could see in his eyes that he feared my response.

"A blindfold applied by any hand would be as good," I answered, giving no sign of recognition.

Just as Caiaphas was about to tie the cloth around my eyes, another man was quietly ushered into the chamber. I recognized him as the father who had been banished on the day I first met Judas.

"As a learned man," Caiaphas spoke, "you will already know the test." The knotted cloth was pulled tight and I could see no more.

"Who is this man?" Joseph shouted. "Let him be identified."

"You know the test Joseph," Caiaphas answered, his patience all but expired. I was turned by the shoulders, until I had no way of knowing which way I faced. A heavy blow to the stomach knocked me to the floor and then, one or more people spat on my head.

"Prophesy now Nazarene," Caiaphas addressed the assembly. "Who was it that struck you?"

I was certain that it had been the banished father, but wanted no part in their game.

"See! He remains silent - he can't tell," the Scribe shouted. Others joined in with support for Caiaphas and his actions.

"Brothers, Brothers!" Joseph call out. "This isn't the way for spiritual leaders to act!"

"Joseph!" Caiaphas shouted him down. "We've had cause to mention your conduct before and we don't wish to repeat ourselves. This Nazarene stands before us, condemned by his own words and worthy of death."

Joseph wouldn't be silenced. "No council judgment can be pronounced during the hours of darkness - it is written!"

"We are well aware of the Law, brother Joseph," Caiaphas replied in a very clipped manner. "No judgment WILL be delivered before daybreak - then he'll be taken in front of Pilate."

"What justice is this?" Joseph shouted across the hall. "Pilate only has two choices - freedom or crucifixion! What crime has this man committed? What actual harm has he done? Where are his accusers - they should be present?"

"Officers of the Court!" Caiaphas called out. "Brother Joseph refuses to take the advice of the Leader of the Temple, so by decree, he should be escorted from the hall!" I could hear the scuffle of feet but knew that any resistance by Joseph would be useless.

"Now Nazarene" Caiaphas spoke, turning his attention to me in almost an affectionate tone. "You will be taken to a holding cell until dawn. Then the Procurate General will decide your fate." With that, I was dragged unceremoniously from the chamber, the blindfold still in place. Just before throwing me forward into the cell, my sandals and the blindfold were removed. The gaoler lit the small oil lamp above the door and threw a bucket of water over me. His action was one of kindness, since my hair had fallen over my eyes and the congealed blood held it in place. The water washed away the blood and afforded me a small but welcome drink.

The cell appeared forgotten and little used. A lattice of stretched-leather provide a narrow sleeping bench, though sleep was the furthest thing from my mind. I lay on my side since my arms were still tightly bound behind my back. Several times through the night, I heard officers approach the door and look through the tiny window.

"Don't worry Nazarene," one called through. "Twenty others have been brought before the assembly. You won't be the only one stretched out to dry." It was cruel comfort. So, despite the officer's offer of a peaceful withdrawal from the supper room, a broad sweep of the hills was being made. I wondered who else might join me in the cell. During the night I heard a constant coming and going, but I remained alone.

Suddenly the cell door was thrown open and Caiaphas entered. With him were two soldiers and the Court Scribe.

Before I could attempt to rise, the soldiers seized me where I lay.

"I've come to learn more about your teaching," Caiaphas reasonably offered, while the soldiers pulled up my tunic, exposing the backs of my legs. In his hands were a couple of lemons and a narrow stick that he crisply twitched in the air. The soldiers held me firmly against the bed.

"I've nothing to give, that you might accept, Caiaphas," I barely answered with my face pressed hard against the leather straps.

"Come now, you're too modest?" he cajoled. "A man who it is *claimed* can raise the dead? A man who is said to be able to manifest bread and fish from the air - to feed hundreds?"

"If you know this, then what words could I offer that would satisfy the Leader of the Temple." As I spoke Caiaphas cut one of the lemons and tasted the juice. Satisfied at its taste, he smiled.

"My own," he offered forward the lemon. Even if I had wanted to drink, my body was held immobile by the soldiers. Sensing I had no interest in tasting his fruit, Caiaphas pulled my head up from the bed and squeezed some juice between my lips. The bitter fluid was a welcome relief, despite the circumstance.

"I have estates along the Galilee," he calmly explained. "I don't suppose you knew that. The Romans have been very generous to their friends."

"And some are greater 'friends' than others," I answered, showing my distaste for his collaboration.

He pulled back, disappointed with my response.

"You see, you don't understand! If it weren't for the Temple Leaders, half our nation would have been sold into slavery. Who do you think has maintained the peace - it's not the Romans! It's us, the Sanhedrin. We've kept the twelve tribes together."

"And should the people be grateful?" I asked, thinking of the thousands who had been driven off the land by their Greek and Roman overlords. One of the soldiers brought the point of his elbow down hard between my shoulders. Caiaphas looked playfully, as if to suggest his treatment might be too rough for one of my 'refinement'.

"Yes, they should," he answered without hesitation. "We save lives - countless Jewish lives. You create turmoil and, by your actions, many will die."

He came back and sat by my head, casually cutting open the second lemon. Carefully, he pulled aside the hair lying on my neck and rubbed one half of the lemon against my nape.

"This will help keep you cool," he spoke thoughtfully. "I hate the heat at this time of year, don't you?" Although he was directing his words towards me, he didn't really expect an answer. This was some scenario he had already worked out before coming into the cell and I was little more than an observer to his performance. It was true the juice against my skin did feel cooler, but I knew my comfort was the furthest thing from Caiaphas' mind.

"I find it helps on the backs of the legs as well," he continued as he rubbed the lemon behind both my knees. "Is that better?" he asked standing up and then lightly blowing against my legs. Almost in a single action, he turned around and brought the stick fiercely down against the backs of my legs. The sudden pain caught me by surprise and I cried out.

"Am I wrong?" he smiled, inquiring about the cooling action. The narrowness of the stick cut through my flesh and mingled with the lemon juice. Even if I had had warning, I couldn't have failed to cry out. "Good", he almost cooed. "I'd hate to think my little talk was boring you."

"What do you want from me," I asked as the lemon juice stung deep.

"A small token, that's all," he offered.

"Another game?" I asked. Even before I had completed the sentence, the stick again cut into my leg. This time I didn't cry out.

"You must learn to take me more seriously, Yeshua ben Joseph," Caiaphas spoke with concern.

"What token?" I asked through gritted teeth.

"Nothing big," he casually replied. "A small miracle perhaps?"

"A miracle?"

"Heal the wound." As he spoke, he directed the juice into the open cut - as if to emphasize his point. "Let me see it and I'll plead for leniency on your behalf."

"You ask for so little, High Priest?" I answered.

"If it is so little, then let me see the blood stop and the cut disappear."

"There would be no point," I spoke downwards through the leather straps.

"Why so you say that? Is your life worth so little?"

"Only my Father in Heaven knows my true worth," I answered.

"Yet you say it is so little?"

"Compared to the healing of your heart, it is." The next stroke came against my bare feet and the pain was beyond anything I had known before.

"You forget yourself Nazarene! I'm the elected leader of the Temple and you are a wandering Rabbi - about to die like a common and forgotten criminal. Help me understand."

"Help *you* understand?"

"Yes. This Kingdom of Heaven, we've heard you speak of - why do men who have studied the scriptures all their lives, why do they not see it?"

"Perhaps you should ask them," I answered. Again the stick bit sharply into the flesh behind my knees.

"But I ask you," Caiaphas spoke softly but without compromise.

"Because they have not studied with their hearts."

"Ah yes - the teaching of the Heart.   Where do you think civilization would be, if we all acted on our heart's impulse - there would be chaos."

"You speak of emotion, I speak of the Wisdom of the Heart." Caiaphas paced a few moments before responding.

"Sit him up and leave," he abruptly ordered.

"But, that would be against Temple Law.   With no witness...," the Scribe interrupted.

"Mikhael the Scribe, you forget yourself!" Caiaphas cut him short.

"Yes Temple Leader," the Scribe timidly conceded, before ushering out the two guards.   Before leaving, the Scribe looked towards Caiaphas to see that this action would be wise.   Caiaphas nodded, by way of conciliation and we were left alone.   Leaning back against the cold wall, the lemon juice was pressed deeper into the cuts and I sharply pulled away in pain.

"It's been a good season for lemons," Caiaphas offered in consideration.   "The passion fruits however, are another question." He paced back and forward in front of me before speaking.

"You trouble me Nazarene," he spoke, sitting down beside me as though we were old acquaintances.   "The Baptist caused trouble, but he was a circus act.   He was an obvious trouble-maker and not difficult to keep an eye on.   If your enemy beats his shield and shouts at the top of his voice, you can always get a good night's sleep. If he becomes quiet, then it's time to raise one eye.   You are far more dangerous."   He stopped to suck the juice from his lemon.   "Your teaching is far more dangerous.   You talk in riddles and riddles stay in the mind.   The danger with this, is that fire can break out at any time."

"If your house is built of stone, why should you fear a small fire," I asked, sensing he really did want to understand.

"Because it isn't controllable and in these times, that would be a recipe for massive bloodshed - something the Temple doesn't want to see. Your teaching is too irresponsible. You light the parched ground and say 'it is God's will' where the flames leap."

"Through fire, new growth is generated," I simply stated, recognizing his entrenched point of view.

"And that's why you cannot be allowed to live, Yeshua ben Joseph. For Israel to live, you, and those like you - must die." With that, he took the corner of his robe and gently brushed the blood from my face.

"I've had reports of your talks, you know," he spoke with consolation. *"Whoever tries to hold onto his life will forfeit it, but whoever gives up his life will preserve it?* Fine words - and I look forward to a demonstration of your words - tomorrow."

Without a further word, he stood up and walked out of the cell. Immediately the guards returned to lock the cell and once again, I was left in darkness.

I lay there understanding how my freedom had become a threat to Caiaphas' office and the entire Temple Hierarchy.

Just before dawn, a pebble landed at my feet. I looked to the narrow window high above.

"Yeshua?" I heard a faint voice call from the street. "Yeshua, it's Elouise."

"I can hear you," I answered with immense relief at hearing a familiar voice. Elouise was one of the women Paul had introduced. The sound of a woman's voice eased my pain. My shoulders ached from having my arms tied back and the lemon juice reminded me of Caiaphas' 'talk'.

"Peter sent me with a message."

"They've captured twenty others," I called back.

"I thought it was more. Everyone has gone into hiding and it's hard to tell," she rushed her words in case she was discovered. "Joseph has gone to Pilate, to plead for you."

"I saw him last night," I answered.

"Peter says to tell you that, if there is to be a crucifixion, he's found a liquid - it'll cause you to fall into a deep sleep." She waited for my reply, but the reality of actually being crucified stopped my tongue. "Joseph's gone to persuade the Romans not to break your legs, so that you can breathe - then you'll be taken down. One of us will offer the liquid to you on a sponge....." At this point she broke off as a distant voice called out.

"Hold there!" the voice shouted, but Elouise didn't wait. Soon after I heard her feet escaping down the street, many others followed in pursuit.

Was this really the sum total of my life - arrested and thrown into prison like a common criminal? Tomorrow might be my last - left hanging to dry beneath the Judaean sun. Were the breaths in my chest already numbered? How could I have been so wrong? Could all those wise men that taught me *all* subject to a collective illusion? Surely that couldn't be! Perhaps Joseph's plan to replace the Sanhedrin *had* been God's true plan and I had been instrumental in subverting the divine scheme? How endless the hours seemed now, yet the dawn all too soon came and went.

In the morning, Caiaphas himself lead the armed guard. The ropes around my arms were released and a searing pain shot through my shoulders and neck as the arms swung helplessly forward.

"We don't want the Romans to think that we aren't civilized, do we," Caiaphas explained. Having said that, they all withdrew from the cell, leaving me alone and the door open. I wondered what new trickery this might be! A woman, covered by a rough shawl and torn dress, entered. It was Mary, my wife! She drew back on seeing me, her head held in horror.

"What have they done, Yeshu!" she barely whispered.

"Mary, you're safe," I spoke, moving to hold her. My arms failed to raise, due to the pain and remained hanging limply at my sides. Mary came forward and put her warm arms around me. Her frail body seemed almost broken as she clung desperately to me. "You shouldn't have come - to see me like this."

"You're so right, Yeshu" she spoke, smiling through her tears. "You don't know how to talk to women. They're leaving us alone - it's the men they want. Your mother has escaped to Ephesus, but I had to come."

"I'm sorry."

"Don't be," she spoke trying to stem the tears.

"Don't you see - I'm responsible!   If they'd chosen James instead of me...."

"James wouldn't have touched as many hearts as you," she softly spoke. "I may not understand your purpose, but one thing I do know - you have to follow your heart. - A wise man from the East once told me that," she teased.   What a treasure I had in Mary and what pure love she carried.

"It's not dying I fear," I spoke to ease her pain.   "Death holds no mystery for me.   Its the possib....the probability, of *any* man willingly killing another that hurts - and in such a way."

"The men have all fled," she sobbed into my chest.

"All?" I asked in disbelief.

"Perhaps a handful remain" she spoke, wiping the tears from her dirt-strewn face and looking to the guards at the open door. "The Sanhedrin are everywhere. The women have been allowed to pass, but the men...," she shook her head so that she wouldn't have to speak the words. I held her close against me, despite the pain. The warmth of her body made me yearn for my youth and the shores of Galilee.

"Joseph has gone to plead with Pilate," I whispered.   This wasn't news to Mary and she didn't look hopeful.

"It's a gamble," she said.   "All he can offer, is that there'll be no armed uprising - but the men have already gone!"

"He's a politician," I offered.   "They sell sunshine on the darkest night."

Mary wouldn't be persuaded, but offered no protest.

"Forgive me?" I pleaded.

"Forgive?"

"For sending you to my mother, all this....."

"There's nothing to forgive" she whispered.

"There is. A husband you knew for barely one night....."

"You had no choice - and the night we had, was sweeter than a Nightingale's song." Her eyes held no blame, no regret.

"I never understood how Samson could be taken so easily by Delilah - now I know.   The pure love of Woman knows depths unknown to Men. Why are we so unable to feel such love?"

"You will *always* be with me..." she spoke cupping my face in her right hand, while her left gently caressed her stomach.

"You mean...?" I spoke with complete joy, forgetting my situation for an instant.

"Yes," she answered as a parent might answer a child. "It may only have been one night, but now the sweetest fruit grows."

"You never sent word?"

"I couldn't be sure, at first," she answered, placing my hand on her stomach.

"But when you were?"

"You had your work," she simply answered. "Whether you're right or wrong, you're still my husband."

"That's enough" Caiaphas called from the door. "It's time to go." Two guards stepped forward to help Mary from the room.

"I was always so certain, but now...." I spoke, looking at her tear-stained face and feeling the full weight of my destiny.

"You must be certain!" she implored. "Believe. If you're wrong, your whole life has been a lie - how can that be! Believe, Yeshu my love." As she spoke, one of the guards took her roughly by the arm and pulled her from the cell.

"My Uncle is far wiser than I ever gave him credit" I called after her. "It was his choice that we marry. Perhaps I should have listened to him in other matters. Mary, I wronged him. Will you tell him?"

"I will" her voice carried back down the stone corridor. "God be with you, Yeshu my husband - my love!"

"Enough!" Caiaphas interrupted. "There's a lot of business to take care of today and you'll be first. And, if it's any comfort, you won't be the last!" Caiaphas spoke with the satisfaction of having arrested many others.

It was less than half an hour's journey to Pilate's Palace, but Caiaphas made a point of traveling at the slowest pace. Along the route, crowds had formed and he wanted everyone to see the futility of angering the Temple Guardians. Many spat in my direction, yet I could see the fear in their faces. Evident among the crowd, were the women of our group. Held back by the guards, they held their arms open towards me. I saw none of the men, only Peter. His head was covered by a dark-striped shawl and his face was very haggard. He held back from the front of the crowd and traveled a short distance alongside us. A woman I didn't recognize, threw a cloth soaked in cold water and I gratefully wiped my face before it could be torn from my hands.

"Blasphemers don't deserve to drink good Judaean water" Caiaphas called out, so that the crowd should know my crime. The woman had tears in her eyes and shook her head repeatedly in denial. This morning was hotter than usual and an air of unreality hung in the air. As we approached the Citadel, I could see members of the Sanhedrin. They were busily organizing small groups of people, so that their voice could be added to the protest. Finally we arrived at the base of the stark white walls. Above us, ten or more Roman dignitaries appeared to be waiting for our arrival. Sat in the forefront, was the man I took to be Pilate. Above his raised podium, a lavishly embroidered red canopy moved gently in the morning breeze. One of the men at his side drew Pilate's attention to our approaching guard. He put aside the scrolls he had been reading and formally washed his hands in the shallow basin at his side.

"Good day, Caiaphas," he casually spoke, while drying his hands.

"Good morning Governor General," Caiaphas called upward, affecting his most cordial tone.

"The weather is set fair for Rome," Pilate spoke wistfully looking to the sky.

"How soon before you leave?" Caiaphas inquired, as though he had nothing more important on his mind.

"Six weeks," he answered. "Would you wish it sooner?"

"I'm deeply offended, Governor General," Caiaphas answered with a smile and some sincerity. "The Sanhedrin knows its friends. Four years is too long for any many to be away from the bosom of his family."

"Of course, of course," Pilate dismissed the pleasantries. "I was told you were bringing an enemy of Judaea before me, yet all I see is this sad and ragged figure. Could your nation's safety be threatened by one so thin?"

"No one has ever accused the viper of being overweight for it's purpose," Caiaphas answered with a sly grin. Pilate also smiled. These two were practiced opponents and knew each other's strengths.

"It's still a sad day that should take you away from your blessed duties," Pilate gently goaded. "And isn't this one of your most sacred holidays?"

"It is one of our most sacred *'festivals'*," Caiaphas corrected.

"But I heard of no crimes committed during the night" Pilate spoke, suppressing a yawn. "Who is this poor traveler you've brought?"

"If he wasn't a criminal, the Sanhedrin wouldn't have brought him to you for judgment, Governor General," Caiaphas spoke with no intention of elaborating further.

"And what Law has he broken?"

"He has been judged a criminal against Roman Law and we ask that sentence be officially passed," Caiaphas answered by rote. Pilate smiled to the Generals beside him.

"It's heartening to see the Sanhedrin so concerned with the interests of Rome, but surely I must be told the crime?"

"This trouble maker has caused insurrection in the Temple grounds. He has terrified honest men." Caiaphas looked to his supporting Sanhedrin members and they nodded in considered agreement. "He has been questioned by the Elders and their judgment is guided by divine grace."

"Naturally," Pilate emphasized without conviction. "But matters of divine grace are no concern of the Imperial Courts."

"Normally that would be correct," Caiaphas corrected.

"- But these are exceptional times?" Pilate responded, knowing his adversary.

"Precisely," Caiaphas acknowledged with a shrug and a regretful smile.

"I can only pass judgment if Roman law has been broken," Pilate firmly stated, hoping that that would be an end to it.

"He claims to be the King of the Jews!" a voice called out from the crowd. Pilate looked to Caiaphas, who again shrugged his shoulders - as if he was merely complying with the people's demands.

"The rule of Kingship is only sanctioned by Caesar!" another voice called out. I recognized the voice as the Temple Scribe who had administered to my hearing. Other Sanhedrin voices echoed the same call, though they were strategically scattered among the crowd. "This man Yeshua, claims that Herod - appointed by Rome -, is a false King," Caiaphas explained.

"Tetrarch Herod - not King," Pilate firmly corrected.

"As you say, Governor General," Caiaphas unconvincingly conceded.

"And he's openly said that we shouldn't pay the Roman taxes!" This voice, I also recognized. Again it was the banished father - now wearing far finer cloth that when I had first seen him on that Galilean hill. Beside him were newly won friends that looked familiar from the night before. If Judas hadn't stepped forward on that fateful day, how different this day might have been.

"And what do you say?" Pilate directly addressed me. "Do you claim to be the King of the Jews? More importantly, have you told any man not to pay Caesar's taxes?" I had nothing to say and remained silent. Why should I lend my energy to these imaginary charges. The consequences were dire, but I couldn't be untrue to my own light.

"These are very serious charges," Pilate spoke with a laugh in his voice, prompting me to deny them. "I'd like an answer." I remained silent. One of the Generals approached Pilate from behind and spoke a few words in confidence. Pilate nodded in agreement with the suggestion and then, began to pace back and forth, before addressing Caiaphas.

"Bring him inside and I'll question him," Pilate called down. By 'question', it was understood 'punish'. The Sanhedrin looked among themselves, uncertain as to what they should to do. No one moved forward.

"What's the problem, Caiaphas?" Pilate called down with undue concern. The Leader of the Temple smiled awkwardly, not knowing how to explain.

"We have no objection to this man being 'questioned' by your good self, Procurate General. It's just that....." Caiaphas broke off, unable to express his thoughts. Pilate slapped his forehead as if suddenly realizing some truth.

"Of course!" he spoke. "It's the time of the Festival and you would be defiling yourself by entering the household of an unclean - I mean - Gentile?" Caiaphas smiled apologetically, but Pilate *had* spoken the truth. The Governor General spoke briefly to an aide. Moments later, I was being dragged through the fortified Palace gates by several large Roman soldiers.

"You will have my answer by midday, High Priest," I heard Pilate call out from somewhere above.

"May God guide your decision," Caiaphas replied.

"But which God?" Pilate answered lightly. "We Romans have so many."

In the shadows of the inner courtyard, I felt the eyes of a hooded-man watch from behind a long colonnade. It was Joseph! He was keeping out of direct sight of the Sanhedrin at the gate. The soldier in command, took a riding crop and rested it against my chest. "I've tamed many a wild horse in my time," he spoke with menace. "Wandering Jews should be a little easier to harness. So, when our Governor asks you to speak - I expect to hear a little bird sing." He put his face very close to mine and the acrid aroma of body sweat and heavy musk, caused me to narrow my eyes. "You'll do more than wince if you don't bring a smile to the Governor's face!"

Pilate and his entourage approached, laughing at some private joke.

"I've heard it said that you're the King of the Jews?" he questioned in a merry mood. I remained silent as his Generals walked around me, as if inspecting a new acquisition for their stables. "Are you the King of the Jews as they claim?" I remained silent. The slightest of gestures from Pilate sent the whip biting across the side of my face. The strike caused blood to seep into my left ear and in moments, I was completely deaf in that ear. A narrow trickle of blood ran down my neck and almost immediately, small biting flies came to investigate. Pilate casually watched a bird fly overhead, before returning to me.

"How can I help you, if you don't respond?" he asked with genuine concern for my well-being. "A life raft is passing in front of you, Jew. Reach out and grab it! I'll ask you one more time - are you, or do you claim to be, the King of the Jews?"

"Is this your question?" I asked, my voice weak from the previous night's exertions. He leaned forward so that I should speak louder. I repeated the question.

"Am I a Jew?" he replied with amused contempt. "I know nothing, except what your accusers have said. Your own people and Chief Priest brought you here." He turned to his entourage and opened his arms. "Am I a Jew, he asks." Everyone laughed - his close friends because they appreciated his wit and the others because they feared his power. "What have you done that they should seek such vengeance? If truth be told, if Caiaphas was a Roman, he'd be one of our most feared Gladiators in the Coliseum. If I weren't the Roman Procurate, *I* might even think twice about crossing him! I've rarely seen him so eager to see the blood of one of his own countrymen? So I ask again..."

"My Kingdom isn't of this world," I quietly spoke.

"Kingdom!" Pilate spoke in amused surprise.. "You stand before me, in rags, your hair matted with blood - and you dare talk of a Kingdom?"

"If it *was* of this world, the streets of Jerusalem would already be flowing with blood."

"Is this a threat I hear?" Pilate asked, leaning closer and his eyes narrowing.

"No threat," I answered. "You know this truth, because your soldiers assisted the Sanhedrin last night." Pilate stood back and looked at me anew.

"So that's what it was. It was you?" he said, suddenly understanding.

"We simply provided an armed escort for the Temple," one of the Generals interjected by way of defense.

"Why wasn't I fully informed?" Pilate quietly spoke, as if musing to himself. The General appeared to fear for his life?

"A formality" the General nervously offered. "They wanted one man seized, but said that his friends might react."

"And did they 'react'?" Pilate quietly asked. His question sounded innocent enough, but the jollity that had been there only moments before, was now a distant memory.

"One man raised his sword," the General quietly answered.

"And how many soldiers did you take to suppress this 'one man'?" Pilate held up a hand and inspected the backs of his fingernails against the sun.

The General looked ashamed at the ground and avoided answering. Pilate turned from his fingernails and watched him for some moments.

"I was informed this morning that an *entire* Cohort left the safety of the City walls?" Pilate spoke more loudly, affecting an air of nonchalance.

"The Sanhedrin had heard rumors that several armed groups might be sleeping close to the city walls," the General sheepishly offered by way of explanation. "You were asleep and we didn't want to disturb you, Governor General."

"Instead, I wake to find that six hundred of Rome's finest, have left the barracks - at the most dangerous time of the year! And you didn't want to disturb me?" Pilate enjoyed the awkward silence that cornered his General.

"You will have my baton before sundown, Governor General," the man suddenly announced. Pilate didn't object and by the reaction from the other Generals, the man had received a lenient judgment.

"Now, where were we?" Pilate turned to me. "Ah yes, we were talking about Kingdoms and armed escorts. This Kingdom," he spoke confidentially, putting an arm around my shoulders. "If it's not Judaea, then where?" Being the taller man, I stood erect so that he couldn't easily rest his arm. As I straightened up, the dry blood across the backs of my legs cracked open and the sand-flies and lemon juice immediately made their presence known.

"As close as your heartbeat," I answered.

"So you don't deny you're a King, as accused?"

"I deny nothing," I answered truthfully. "My destiny is to bear witness to Truth."

"Then I feel sorry for you Rabbi, because the only truth you'll bear witness to, is the hatred of your own people." We had begun to trade words and I knew I wouldn't be able to make him understand. Once again I fell silent.

"Do you know a man named Joseph?" he casually asked. "From Arimathea I believe?" By the reaction in my eyes, he knew I was acquainted with Joseph.

"He's an old acquaintance," Pilate continued, regardless. "Supplies wines and cloth for the Garrison. While my soldiers were out collecting 'night orchids'," he spoke with a wry smile towards his retiring General, "this tradesman came to me with a strange story." Seeing that he had everyone's rapt attention, he became overly theatrical. "He spoke of King's and armies! He said that the Sanhedrin might even be replaced? Would you know anything about this?" I had no answer that would serve any purpose, so remained silent.

"Of course you don't," he answered his own question. "We have an understanding, this Joseph and I." Still he looked for confirmation, but I gave none. He took a few paces towards the garrison gate and then turned. "I care little, but can't you understand? These people want you crucified!"

"Where a light shines in the night, dark angry shadows dance close by," I answered, since it appeared he sincerely wanted to understand. "Out of fear for the shadows, should I deny my light?" He shook his head as though I didn't understand the practicality of the situation. Casually, he walked over to the soldier in charge and carefully inspected the side of his leather helmet.

"You're from Athens aren't you, Septimus," he asked as though it had some bearing on the discussion. The soldier moved uneasily as he replied.

"Just outside Athens, Governor General."

"Good," Pilate responded thoughtfully. "Do you think Greek or Roman education is better?" The soldier smiled broadly, now understanding Pilate's drift.

"Roman education, Governor General. Definitely Roman!"

"Good," Pilate replied stepping back. "See to it that the Rabbi receives our *finest* education." The soldier ran off and quickly returned with a leather flail. The flail had seven leather tails with thin metal strips woven into their tips.

The first strike tore the shirt from my back, allowing the blood to flow unhindered down to my loin cloth and beyond. Several more fierce lashings took the strength from my legs and I sank slowly to the ground.

"This isn't for our benefit," Pilate explained. "No, this is for *your* benefit."

"Please don't trouble yourself on my behalf," I spoke with what little remaining strength I could muster. Pilate smiled.

"I like you Rabbi. There are so few Jews who make me laugh," he generously offered. "No, it's not for our pleasure. If I take you in front of the Sanhedrin without showing that we've seriously 'questioned' you, they'll immediately demand crucifixion. However, if I can show that I've tried to make you confirm their accusations and you still haven't - then they have no case. So you see, it's lucky that I like you."

Explaining this, the other Generals also seemed to look on me with new found kindness.

"Rabbi, I know little about your religions and care less, but I can see that you're an innocent among wolves." He walked over to one of his soldiers and touched the shining breastplate. "At the head of my legions, I've seen rivers of blood. Yet somehow a chill crosses my heart at the prospect of handing you over to these people. Help me?"

"We each have our purpose, Governor General," I replied. He became impatient with my response, yet appeared to have reached a decision. "Bring him!" he ordered as he briskly walked away.

I was raised to my feet and then dragged up the marbled stairs and back along a porticoed walkway. Soon after, we arrived at the podium from which Pilate had spoken to the crowd. Below us, the crowd had grown considerably. Barely able to stand, one of the Generals lightly supported me from the side. Among the crowd, I recognized several of Peter's right hand men and many of the women. The women had organized a body of protest and were being driven back by mounted Sanhedrin officers. Several of the women lay on the ground having already fallen beneath the hooves of the horses. One small group surrounded a badly bleeding woman I believed to be Anna, the woman who looked after Paul. From the demeanor of the women around her, I presumed her to be dead. The Sanhedrin orchestrated a silence for Pilate to speak.

"People of Judaea," Pilate loudly announced.   "I have questioned this man and find he has no case to answer."

"Crucify, crucify!" the shout went up.   It was too clear a response for spontaneity and, judging by the way many of the Sanhedrin faced the crowd instead of Pilate, considerable pressure had already been brought to bear.

"Crucify the Nazarene - or should we not pay the taxes?" one called out.

Pilate looked to see who had spoken, but couldn't identify any particular person.

"He said nothing about taxes," Pilate directly addressed Caiaphas.   "He's an innocent man."

An aide beside Caiaphas replied.   "Governor Pilate, we have hundreds of witnesses who are prepared testify against him.   Are you supporting his claim that we shouldn't pay Caesar's taxes?"

Pilate smiled.   "When you arrived here, you appeared more interested that he claimed to be a King.   Now you're more interested in protecting Roman coffers!   I'll commend you to Caesar when I return to Rome."

"If he isn't crucified, it may be *many* years before you see Rome!" another voice called out from the crowd.   Pilate became furious at this.

"Who said that?   Soldiers, bring him to me!" he shouted.   A General at his side came forward to inspect the crowd, but had no idea where to send his men.

"That man voiced the feeling of the people, Governor General," Caiaphas offered.   "Would you punish a whole people?" The question was put because every Jew already felt himself persecuted by Rome, simply by forced-occupation of our Promised Land.   Pilate recognized the true intent of the words and refused to answer.   "If the Nazarene isn't punished, the Sanhedrin may not be able to guarantee the actions of it's people," he spoke in less than veiled threat.

"These are dangerous words, Rabbi," Pilate threatened.

"We live in dangerous times," Caiaphas concurred.   Both men held each other's gaze.   The General who had stepped forward to inspect the crowd, leaned close and whispered in Pilate's ear.   Pilate quickly acknowledged the words and then dismissed the man to his rear.

"As Governor of Judaea," he began. "I have a privilege on this, your Festive day. I have the privilege of releasing one of my prisoners."

The aide beside Caiaphas, conferred quickly with the High Priest. Caiaphas smiled.

"If you know this Law, you will also know that the privilege of release is yours - the naming of *which* prisoner, is ours," Caiaphas called up. Pilate looked to his General for confirmation. An almost imperceptible nod of the head indicated that Caiaphas was indeed right.

"Then I'll put it to the people of Judaea," Pilate spoke broadly, going over the head of the Temple Leader. "People of Judaea, I have four prisoners in my cells. Three are Zealots, one being their leader Barabus. He has murdered many an honest Jew and deserves the full weight of the law. All stand condemned by your courts and the penalty is death. Only this man Yeshua, has not taken life - and would be found innocent by any Roman court."

Before he could say more, a faint call for my name came up from the crowd below. The men dare not be shown, but the women openly called out. Scuffles immediately broke out and the call was drowned, as a louder call for Barabus rang out. In the crowd, I now saw Peter being attacked with stones and bleeding from a cut on his head. Pilate became incensed at this disregard for his rule. At any moment a full scale riot was going to break out. Caiaphas moved among the crowd and went through the motions of attempting to subdue the trouble makers. To everyone who could see, especially Pilate, it was clear that Caiaphas was well pleased with the situation.

"Is this how you control your own people?" Pilate asked, the frustration showing in his voice.

Caiaphas shrugged his shoulders and pointed to the outbreaks. "I'm merely a servant of the people - and you have heard their voice," he offered with little conviction. Recognizing the real possibility of his not returning to Rome in the foreseeable future, Pilate had little choice. He stepped forward to speak.

"People of Judaea," he spoke solemnly. "This day, I, Pontius Pilate, Governor General of Judaea and appointed by his Imperial Eminence, Tiberius Caesar - sanction the penalty of crucifixion for the prisoner Yeshua. He will be escorted to the Hill of Skulls where the decreed penalty will be carried out before sundown this day." With that, Pilate held the palms of his hands open directly towards Caiaphas. "My hands are clean," he accused. Then, he held his hands high so that everyone in the crowd could also see.

Almost immediately, I found myself being dragged forward at the end of a rope by one of the Centurions. The rope was loose enough around my neck that I could easily have slipped its hold, but for what reason? To some small degree it kept the flies away from the blood at my throat and so provided some relief. Around me marched a phalanx of Roman soldiers, alert to any reaction from the milling crowd. Their spears slapped in unison against their polished metal breast-plates, while their swords hung loosely at their side. As we passed through the city perimeter walls, three Sanhedrin officials fell into step directly ahead of me. Caiaphas was ceremoniously offered command of the detachment and, as was the custom, deferred to the commanding Centurion. Before we moved off again, Caiaphas asked for a moment to speak with me. The Centurion was nervous, because the crowd had become increasingly hostile and he wanted to continue without delay.

"What now King of the Jews!" a voice from the crowd called out. "Where are your brave armed men now?"

"Stand back!" the Captain of the guard shouted. "Have respect for the crucifixions!"

"Since you've shamed the Temple, Yeshua," Caiaphas spoke so that only I could hear. "There is something you should know." I looked into his eyes and saw a mixture of hatred and envy. "Joseph the Arimathean has been charged with crimes against the Holy Temple - and we have learned about his visit to Pilate." He so wanted me to question him, but it seemed unimportant in the moment. Ahead, I heard the cries of men being pulled up on their crucifixes. He had said I was not the first and wouldn't be the last.

"We don't know what deal he's struck with Pilate - but we will." He spoke with some desperation, not being in complete control.   "And if you think you'll become a martyr, Yeshua ben Joseph - think again!   When you're taken down from the cross, your body will disappear.   Each limb will be taken and buried in different parts of Judaea.   There'll be nothing for your followers to point to - nothing to worship!   You're already a forgotten man, Yeshua ben Joseph!   Think on that as you leave this world!"

He looked for a reaction, but I had none.   Each step towards the Hill of Skulls took me closer to God.   I looked with pity at Caiaphas and saw confusion and fear.   He couldn't comprehend that I held no malice towards him.   He only saw as far as his earth-bound ego and had no understanding of the Love that surpasses all understanding.

When we arrived at the plateau of the hill, nine men already hung against the sky.   Some were already dead and the crows rested nervously on their heads.   Some had only just been crucified before we arrived.   A soldier was fixing the wooden plug to the feet of the most recently crucified, so that the man's feet couldn't be pulled out from their metal spikes.

"A forest with no leaves," I thought.

Lying on my back, the wood felt warm against my naked spine.   Not a single cloud drifted in the sky.   A man either side, stretched my arms outward against the wooden beam.   In a distant awareness I felt a weakness in both my wrists as a spray of warm blood flicked across my face.   My shoulders found a curious familiarity in their position as I was raised towards the sky and thought of the Sanhedrin cell.

Among the Roman guard, I recognized one of the faces.   In moments I recalled - it was Marcellus, the servant from the Capernaeum barracks.   I remembered the wind-swept day he had come and asked a healing for his master's servant.   His faith then, warmed me now.   He looked curiously out of place among the Roman guard as they fought to keep the crowd at bay.

"Are you the Galilean?" the crucified man at my side asked. "The one the Baptist spoke about?"

"I am," I answered.

"Can't you see he's delirious" another crucified man ahead of me spoke, barely able to raise his body and his voice already weak. "He never knew the Baptist!"

"Quiet," the first softly spoke. "We have blood on our hands. This Rabbi only ever spoke of Love and God. If you can, save yourself Rabbi. We aren't worthy to die beside you."

"The pain is so great, yet you tell this stranger to save himself? It's you that's delirious," the second gasped as he hung heavily from the ropes at his arms.

"Quiet," the first one ordered. "Can't you see, this is the man Israel's been waiting for. Rabbi, tell me something that will ease my pain, something to fix my attention on," he pleaded.

I looked to him and he threw his head back to relieve the pressure on his back. His eyes closed in intense suffering.

"It was your destiny that we meet this last day," I spoke to his inner being. "Look to your inner eye and speak the secret name of God. Fix your mind on God. Flesh is but an instant in time, Spirit is eternal."

"And me Rabbi," the second asked giving way to his fear, "Where should I look?"

"It is the same for all men," I answered, sad that he should feel so lost.

At my feet, I watched as an appointed soldier raised his cudgel and crushed the legs of the second man. Unable to raise himself to breath further, the man's stomach shook violently for several moments before his head fell loosely forward.

"I'm afraid, Rabbi," the first called out, as the Soldier moved towards him.

"I'm afraid too," I answered, looking directly forward. "Fix your attention on eternal Soul and whisper God's name." As I spoke, a crushing and dull sound came from my left and he spoke no more. I looked to him and a look of indescribable pain slowly turned to a warm smile, as his head slowly eased forward. In turn, the soldier moved to the base of my crucifix. As he swung the sharp cudgel back to strike, the Captain of the Guard called out for him to stop. The soldier held his swing and looked back. The Captain indicated that my legs were to be left and waved forward a man I now recognized as John.

"Hey, King of the Jews," a Sanhedrin member called out. "How does your Kingdom look from that throne?" Several of the men at the man's side laughed openly, encouraging others to follow suit - but none did. In the crowd, Caiaphas remained silent and troubled.

John moved slowly, as if in pain. His clothes were dirty and torn in several places. From inside his cloak, he took a small glazed container and offered it forward for the soldier to inspect.

"Vinegar to ease his pain," John explained. The soldier looked doubtful. "If his legs aren't to be broken, it's a small gesture..." The soldier looked towards his Captain for confirmation. His commanding officer was distracted by a fight that had broken out between some of the Sanhedrin and the people. Seeing no harm in it, the soldier indicated for John to go ahead and administer the drink. The guard I had recognized as Marcellus, broke away from the broadening scuffle and came determinedly towards us. John took out a small sponge and poured the liquid over it.

"Yeshua, drink" John offered, placing the sponge on a stick and reaching it up to my lips.

"John, why is the world so dark?" I asked.

"You're mistaken Yeshua," he answered anxiously. "Here, drink so that you can sleep."

"Soul never sleeps, it is always present" I answered on recognizing Truth.

"Yeshua, please drink!" he implored. "He won't drink. The suffering has taken his mind," John explained, as Marcellus approached. Marcellus pushed John aside and, taking his spear, thrust it deep under my ribs.

"He'll suffer no more," I heard Marcellus say with love in his heart..............

Paradox is composed of both light and dark. Where the two meet, there grows a Golden Seed. I call it God. -

Yeshua ben Joseph

* * * * * * ✡ * * * * * *

THE Autobiography

ORDER FORM

Amron Press,
Suite 157 - 2496 East Hastings Street,
Vancouver,
British Columbia,
CANADA,
V5K 1Z1

Tel :- (604) 253 3283
Fax :- (604) 253 3233

Please send me_____ copy/copies of
THE Autobiography *of Jesus of Nazareth and the Missing Years,*
for which I enclose an International Money Order or Bank Draft
made out to AMRON PRESS in **Canadian dollars** for the sum of
_____at a cost of $24.95 CAN each, plus shippage *(see below).

I understand that if I am dissatisfied for <u>ANY</u> reason, I may return
the book(s) in salable condition (accompanied by the original receipt
from Amron Press) for an immediate and full refund.   There is NO
TIME LIMIT to this offer and no questions will be asked.

Please print *information below to ensure correct delivery*

Name:_____
Address: _____
City: _____State: _____Area code:_____
Telephone: (___) _____

<u>If books are ordered within Canada</u> 7% G.S.T. must be added to the
cost of the books (i.e.; $26.70 each).   GST Ref : 136051448

* Please add $5 CAN. for following-day shippage by Air mail.   This
applies for upto TEN books.   Units higher than ten will be shipped
free by surface delivery. This offer applies only within U.S.A and
Canada. Regular International Postal rates apply to other countries.

THE Autobiography

ORDER FORM

Amron Press,
Suite 157 - 2496 East Hastings Street,
Vancouver,
British Columbia,
CANADA,
V5K 1Z1

Tel :- (604) 253 3283
Fax :- (604) 253 3233

Please send me_____ copy/copies of
THE Autobiography *of Jesus of Nazareth and the Missing Years,*
for which I enclose an International Money Order or Bank Draft
made out to AMRON PRESS in **Canadian dollars** for the sum of
_____at a cost of $24.95 CAN each, plus shippage *(see below).

I understand that if I am dissatisfied for <u>ANY</u> reason, I may return
the book(s) in salable condition (accompanied by the original receipt
from Amron Press) for an immediate and full refund.   There is NO
TIME LIMIT to this offer and no questions will be asked.

Please print *information below to ensure correct delivery*

Name:_____
Address: _____
City: _____State: _____Area code:_____
Telephone: (___) _____

<u>If books are ordered within Canada</u> 7% G.S.T. must be added to the
cost of the books (i.e.; $26.70 each).   GST Ref : 136051448

* Please add $5 CAN. for following-day shippage by Air mail.   This
applies for upto TEN books.   Units higher than ten will be shipped
free by surface delivery. This offer applies only within U.S.A and
Canada. Regular International Postal rates apply to other countries.

THE Autobiography

ORDER FORM

Amron Press,
Suite 157 - 2496 East Hastings Street,
Vancouver,
British Columbia,
CANADA,
V5K 1Z1

Tel :- (604) 253 3283
Fax :- (604) 253 3233

Please send me_____ copy/copies of
THE Autobiography *of Jesus of Nazareth and the Missing Years,*
for which I enclose an International Money Order or Bank Draft
made out to AMRON PRESS in **Canadian dollars** for the sum of
_____at a cost of $24.95 CAN each, plus shippage *(see below).

I understand that if I am dissatisfied for <u>ANY</u> reason, I may return
the book(s) in salable condition (accompanied by the original receipt
from **A**mron Press) for an immediate and full refund.   There is NO
TIME LIMIT to this offer and no questions will be asked.

Please print *information below to ensure correct delivery*

Name:_____
Address: _____
City: _____State: _____Area code:_____
Telephone: (___) _____

<u>If books are ordered within Canada</u> 7% G.S.T. must be added to the
cost of the books (i.e.; $26.70 each).   GST Ref : 136051448

* Please add $5 CAN. for following-day shippage by Air mail.   This
applies for upto TEN books.   Units higher than ten will be shipped
free by surface delivery. This offer applies only within U.S.A and
Canada. Regular International Postal rates apply to other countries.

THE Autobiography